THE COSMIC PERSPECTIVE

CUSTOM EDITION FOR TCU ARCHAEOASTRONOMY

Taken from:
The Cosmic Perspective
Sixth Edition
By Jeffrey Bennett

Learning Solutions

New York Boston San Francisco
London Toronto Sydney Tokyo Singapore Madrid
Mexico City Munich Paris Cape Town Hong Kong Montreal

Cover Art: Courtesy of PhotoDisc/Getty Images

Taken from:

The Cosmic Perspective, Sixth Edition
By Jeffrey Bennett, et al
Copyright © 2011, 2010, 2008, 2006 by Pearson Education, Inc.
Published by Addison-Wesley
Boston, Massachusetts 02116

This special edition published in cooperation with Pearson Learning Solutions.

Pearson Learning Solutions, 501 Boylston Street, Suite 900, Boston, MA 02116
A Pearson Education Company
www.pearsoned.com

Printed in the United States of America

9 10 11 12 13 V0UD 19 18 17 16 15

0002000102706570 77
RR

ISBN 10: 0-558-94815-4
ISBN 13: 978-0-558-94815-3

DETAILED CONTENTS

DISCOVERING THE UNIVERSE FOR YOURSELF

LEARNING GOALS

We had the sky, up there, all speckled with stars, and we used to lay on our backs and look up at them, and discuss about whether they was made, or only just happened.

—Mark Twain, *Huckleberry Finn*

This is an exciting time in the history of astronomy. A new generation of telescopes is scanning the depths of the universe. Increasingly sophisticated space probes are collecting new data about the planets and other objects in our solar system. Rapid advances in computing technology are allowing scientists to analyze the vast amount of new data and to model the processes that occur in planets, stars, galaxies, and the universe.

One goal of this book is to help *you* share in the ongoing adventure of astronomical discovery. One of the best ways to become a part of this adventure is to do what other humans have done for thousands of generations: Go outside, observe the sky around you, and contemplate the awe-inspiring universe of which you are a part. In this chapter, we'll discuss a few key ideas that will help you understand what you see in the sky.

2.1 PATTERNS IN THE NIGHT SKY

Today we take for granted that we live on a small planet orbiting an ordinary star in one of many galaxies in the universe. But this fact is not obvious from a casual glance at the night sky, and we've learned about our place in the cosmos only through a long history of careful observations. In this section, we'll discuss major features of the night sky and how we understand them in light of our current knowledge of the universe.

What does the universe look like from Earth?

Shortly after sunset, as daylight fades to darkness, the sky appears to slowly fill with stars. On clear, moonless nights far from city lights, more than 2000 stars may be visible to your naked eye, along with the whitish band of light that we call the *Milky Way* (Figure 2.1). As you look at the stars, your mind may group them into patterns that look like familiar shapes or objects. If you observe the sky night after night or year after year, you will recognize the same patterns of stars. These patterns have not changed noticeably in the past few thousand years.

Constellations People of nearly every culture gave names to patterns they saw in the sky. We usually refer to such patterns as constellations, but to astronomers the term has a more precise meaning: A **constellation** is a *region* of the sky with well-defined borders; the familiar patterns of stars merely help us locate the constellations. Just as every spot of land in the continental United States is part of some state, every point in the sky belongs to some constellation.

FIGURE 2.1 This photo shows the Milky Way over Haleakala crater on the island of Maui, Hawaii. The bright spot just below (and slightly left of) the center of the band is the planet Jupiter.

Figure 2.2 shows the borders of the constellation Orion and several of its neighbors.

The names and borders of the 88 official constellations (Appendix H) were chosen in 1928 by members of the International Astronomical Union (IAU). Most of the IAU members lived in Europe or the United States, so they chose names familiar in the western world. That is why the

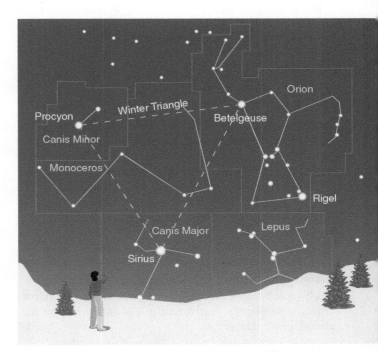

FIGURE 2.2 Red lines mark official borders of several constellations near Orion. Yellow lines connect recognizable patterns of stars within constellations. Sirius, Procyon, and Betelgeuse form a pattern that spans several constellations and is called the *Winter Triangle*. It is easy to see on clear winter evenings.

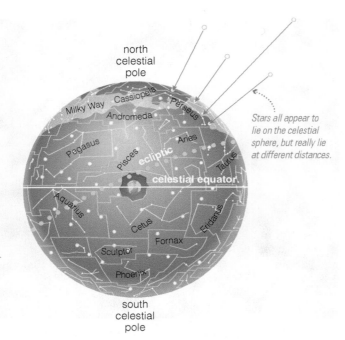

north
celestial
pole

Milky Way
Cassiopeia
Andromeda
Perseus
Pegasus
Aries
ecliptic
Pisces
Taurus
celestial equator
Aquarius
Cetus
Eridanus
Fornax
Sculptor
Phoenix

south
celestial
pole

Stars all appear to
lie on the celestial
sphere, but really lie
at different distances.

FIGURE 2.3 The stars and constellations appear to lie on a celestial sphere that surrounds Earth. This is an illusion created by our lack of depth perception in space, but it is useful for mapping the sky.

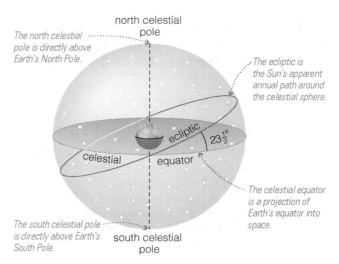

north celestial
pole

The north celestial
pole is directly above
Earth's North Pole.

The ecliptic is
the Sun's apparent
annual path around
the celestial sphere.

ecliptic
$23\frac{1}{2}°$
celestial   equator

The celestial equator
is a projection of
Earth's equator into
space.

The south celestial pole
is directly above Earth's
South Pole.

south celestial
pole

FIGURE 2.4 This schematic diagram shows key features of the celestial sphere.

official names for constellations visible in the Northern Hemisphere can be traced back to civilizations of the ancient Middle East, while Southern Hemisphere constellations carry names that originated with 17th-century European explorers.

Recognizing the patterns of just 20 to 40 constellations is enough to make the sky seem as familiar as your own neighborhood. The best way to learn the constellations is to go out and view them, guided by a few visits to a planetarium and star charts.

The Celestial Sphere The stars in a particular constellation appear to lie close to one another but may be quite far apart in reality, because they may lie at very different distances from Earth. This illusion occurs because we lack depth perception when we look into space, a consequence of the fact that the stars are so far away [Section 1.2]. The ancient Greeks mistook this illusion for reality, imagining the stars and constellations to lie on a great **celestial sphere** that surrounds Earth (Figure 2.3).

We now know that Earth seems to be in the center of the celestial sphere only because it is where we are located as we look into space. Nevertheless, the celestial sphere is a useful illusion, because it allows us to map the sky as seen from Earth. For reference, we identify four special points and circles on the celestial sphere (Figure 2.4).

- The **north celestial pole** is the point directly over Earth's North Pole.

- The **south celestial pole** is the point directly over Earth's South Pole.

- The **celestial equator**, which is a projection of Earth's equator into space, makes a complete circle around the celestial sphere.

- The **ecliptic** is the path the Sun follows as it appears to circle around the celestial sphere once each year. It crosses the celestial equator at a $23\frac{1}{2}°$ angle, because that is the tilt of Earth's axis.

The Milky Way The band of light that we call the *Milky Way* circles all the way around the celestial sphere, passing through more than a dozen constellations. The widest and brightest parts of the Milky Way are most easily seen from the Southern Hemisphere, which probably explains why the Aborigines of Australia gave names to patterns within the Milky Way in the same way other cultures named patterns of stars.

Our Milky Way Galaxy gets its name from this band of light, and the two "Milky Ways" are closely related: *The Milky Way in the night sky traces our galaxy's disk of stars—the galactic plane—as it appears from our location in the outskirts of the galaxy.* Figure 2.5 shows the idea. The Milky Way Galaxy is shaped like a thin pancake with a bulge in the middle. We view the universe from our location a little more than halfway out from the center of this "pancake." In all directions that we look within the pancake, we see the countless stars and vast interstellar clouds that make up the Milky Way in the night sky; that is why the band of light makes a full circle around our sky. The Milky Way appears somewhat wider in the direction of the constellation Sagittarius, because that is the direction in which we are looking toward the galaxy's central bulge. We can observe the distant universe only when we look in directions *away* from the galactic disk, so that there are relatively few stars and clouds to block our view.

The dark lanes that run down the center of the Milky Way contain the densest clouds, and they appear dark because these clouds obscure our view of stars behind them. In fact, these clouds generally prevent us from seeing more than a few thousand light-years into our galaxy's disk. As a result, much of our own galaxy remained hidden from view until just a few

When we look out of the galactic plane (white arrows), we have a clear view to the distant universe.

Galactic plane

Location of our solar system

When we look in any direction into the galactic plane (blue arrows), we see the stars and interstellar clouds that make up the Milky Way in the night sky.

FIGURE 2.5 This painting shows how our galaxy's structure affects our view from Earth.

decades ago, when new technologies allowed us to peer through the clouds by observing forms of light that are invisible to our eyes (such as radio waves and X rays [Section 5.2]).

THINK ABOUT IT

Consider a distant galaxy located in the same direction from Earth as the center of our own galaxy (but much farther away). Could we see it with our eyes? Explain.

The Local Sky The celestial sphere provides a useful way of thinking about the appearance of the universe from Earth. But it is not what we actually see when we go outside. Picture yourself standing in a flat, open field. The sky appears to take the shape of a dome, making it easy to understand why people of many ancient cultures imagined that we lived on a flat Earth under a great dome encompassing the world. We see only half of the celestial sphere at any particular moment from any particular location, while the other half is blocked from view by the ground. The half of the celestial sphere that

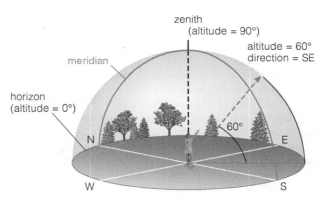

FIGURE 2.6 From any place on Earth, the local sky looks like a dome (hemisphere). This diagram shows key reference points in the local sky. It also shows how we can describe any position in the local sky by its altitude and direction.

you see at any time represents what we call your **local sky**—the sky as seen from wherever you happen to be standing.

Figure 2.6 shows key reference features of the local sky. The boundary between Earth and sky defines the **horizon**. The point directly overhead is the **zenith**. The **meridian** is an imaginary half circle stretching from the horizon due south, through the zenith, to the horizon due north.

We can pinpoint the position of any object in the local sky by stating its **direction** along the horizon (sometimes stated as *azimuth*, which is degrees clockwise from due north) and its **altitude** above the horizon. For example, Figure 2.6 shows a person pointing to a star located in the direction of southeast at an altitude of 60°. Note that the zenith has altitude 90° but no direction, because it is straight overhead.

Angular Sizes and Distances Our lack of depth perception on the celestial sphere means we have no way to judge the true sizes or separations of the objects we see in the sky. However, we can describe the *angular* sizes or separations of objects even without knowing how far away they are.

The **angular size** of an object is the angle it appears to span in your field of view. For example, the angular sizes of the Sun and Moon are each about $\frac{1}{2}°$ (Figure 2.7a). Notice that angular size does not by itself tell us an object's true size, because angular size also depends on distance. The Sun

a The angular sizes of the Sun and the Moon are about 1/2°.

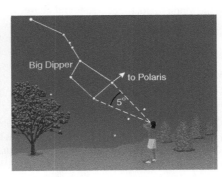

b The angular distance between the "pointer stars" of the Big Dipper is about 5°.

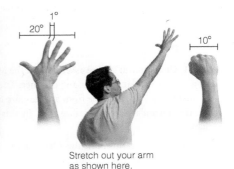

Stretch out your arm as shown here.

c You can estimate angular sizes or distances with your outstretched hand.

FIGURE 2.7 We measure *angular sizes* or *angular distances*, rather than actual sizes or distances, when we look at objects in the sky.

Angular Size, Physical Size, and Distance

If you hold a quarter in front of your eye, it can block your entire field of view. But as you move it farther away, it appears to get smaller and blocks less of your view. Figure 1a summarizes the idea by showing the quarter in cross section, so we can see how its angular diameter decreases with distance.

It's useful to have a formula telling us how an object's angular size depends on its physical size and distance, and we can find the formula with a little mathematical trick that works when the angular size is small. In Figure 1b, we've made the quarter from Figure 1a look like a tiny piece of a circle going all the way around your eye. The radius of the circle is the *distance* from your eye to the quarter, the angle from your eye is the quarter's *angular size*, and we've labeled the quarter's actual diameter as its *physical size*. Now, notice that as long as the angular size is relatively small (less than a few degrees), we can pretend that the quarter's physical size (diameter) is a small piece of the circle we've drawn. This is the trick we needed: The quarter's angular size is now the *same fraction* of the full 360° circle as its physical size is of the circle's physical circumference. Since the circumference of this circle is $2\pi \times (distance)$, we can write what we've found as

$$\frac{\text{angular size}}{360°} = \frac{\text{physical size}}{2\pi \times \text{distance}}$$

Multiplying both sides by 360° and rearranging a bit, we have a formula that allows us to determine angular size when we know physical size and distance:

$$\text{angular size} = \text{physical size} \times \frac{360°}{2\pi \times \text{distance}}$$

This formula is sometimes called the *small-angle formula*, since it is valid only when the angular size is small.

In astronomy, we generally measure an object's angular size and often have a way of determining its distance (we'll discuss distance measurement techniques in later chapters). We can therefore rearrange the formula to calculate physical size. You should confirm that a little algebra tells us that

$$\text{physical size} = \text{angular size} \times \frac{2\pi \times \text{distance}}{360°}$$

The context of a problem will tell you which form of the formula to choose.

EXAMPLE 1: The angular diameter of the Moon is about 0.5° and the Moon is about 380,000 km away. Estimate the Moon's actual diameter.

SOLUTION:

Step 1 Understand: We are asked to find the Moon's actual diameter given its angular diameter and distance. The formula below tells us how to find physical *size* from angular size and distance; we can use this formula once we realize that, in this case, the "size" is a diameter.

Step 2 Solve: We now use the formula to calculate the Moon's physical size (diameter) from the given values of its angular size and distance:

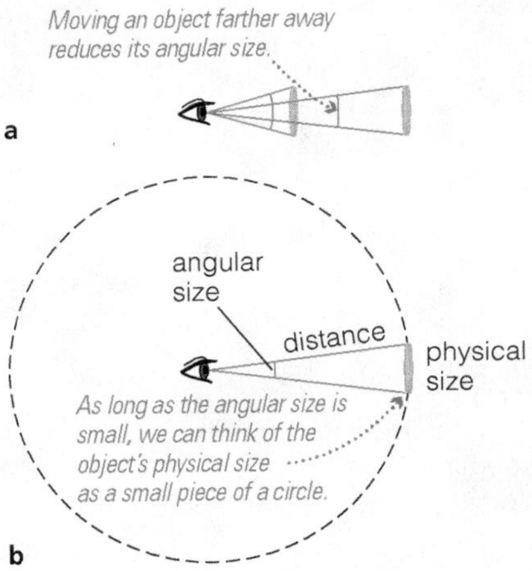

FIGURE 1 Angular size depends on physical size and distance.

$$\text{physical size} = \text{angular size} \times \frac{2\pi \times \text{distance}}{360°}$$

$$= 0.5° \times \frac{2\pi(380,000 \text{ km})}{360°}$$

$$\approx 3300 \text{ km}$$

Step 3 Explain: We have found that the Moon's diameter is about 3300 kilometers. We can check that our answer makes sense by comparing it to the value for the Moon's diameter given in Appendix E. Our estimate of 3300 kilometers is fairly close to the Moon's actual diameter of 3476 kilometers, which we could find by using more precise values for the Moon's angular diameter and distance.

EXAMPLE 2: Suppose the two headlights on a car are separated by 1.5 meters and you are looking at the car from a distance of 500 meters. What is the angular separation of the headlights?

SOLUTION:

Step 1 Understand: In this case we are asked about "separation" between two lights rather than size, but the idea is the same. We simply replace size with separation in the formulas below and we have all the information we need to solve the problem.

Step 2 Solve: Because we know the physical separation and distance in this case, we use the formula in the first form that we found above.

$$\begin{aligned}\text{angular} \\ \text{separation}\end{aligned} = \text{physical separation} \times \frac{360°}{2\pi \times \text{distance}}$$

$$= 1.5 \text{ m} \times \frac{360°}{2\pi(500 \text{ m})} = 0.17°$$

Step 3 Explain: We have found that the angular separation of the two headlights is 0.17°. However, remember that it is more common to express fractions of a degree in arcminutes or arcseconds. There are 60 arcminutes in 1°, so our answer of 0.17° is equivalent to 0.7° × 60 arcmin/1° = 10.2 arcminutes. In other words, the angular separation of the headlights is about 10 arcminutes, which is about $\frac{1}{3}$ of the 30 arcminute (0.5°) angular diameter of the full moon.

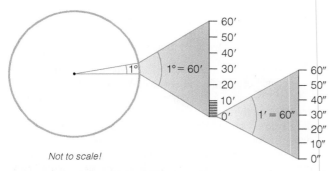

Not to scale!

FIGURE 2.8 We subdivide each degree into 60 arcminutes and each arcminute into 60 arcseconds.

is about 400 times larger in diameter than the Moon, but it has the same angular size in our sky because it is also about 400 times farther away.

The **angular distance** between a pair of objects in the sky is the angle that appears to separate them. For example, the angular distance between the "pointer stars" at the end of the Big Dipper's bowl is about 5° (Figure 2.7b). You can use your outstretched hand to make rough estimates of angles in the sky (Figure 2.7c).

For more precise astronomical measurements, we subdivide each degree into 60 **arcminutes** and subdivide each arcminute into 60 **arcseconds** (Figure 2.8). We abbreviate arcminutes with the symbol ' and arcseconds with the symbol ". For example, we read 35°27'15" as "35 degrees, 27 arcminutes, 15 arcseconds."

THINK ABOUT IT

Children often try to describe the sizes of objects in the sky (such as the Moon or an airplane) in inches or miles, or by holding their fingers apart and saying "it was THIS big." Can we really describe objects in the sky in this way? Why or why not?

Why do stars rise and set?

If you spend a few hours out under a starry sky, you'll notice that the universe seems to be circling around us, with stars moving gradually across the sky from east to west. Many ancient people took this appearance of movement at face

The Moon Illusion

You've probably noticed that the full moon appears to be larger when it is near the horizon than when it is high in your sky. However, this apparent size change is an illusion. If you measure the angular size of the full moon on a particular night, you'll find that it is about the same whether the Moon is near the horizon or high in the sky. The Moon's angular size in the sky depends only on its true size and its distance from Earth. Although this distance varies over the course of the Moon's monthly orbit, it does not change enough to cause a noticeable effect on a single night. You can confirm that the Moon's angular size remains the same by measuring it. You may also be able to make the illusion go away by viewing the Moon upside down between your legs when it is on the horizon.

value, concluding that we lie at the center of a universe that rotates around us each day. Today we know that the ancients had it backward: It is Earth that rotates, not the rest of the universe, and that is why the Sun, Moon, planets, and stars all move across our sky each day.

We can picture the movement of the sky by imagining the celestial sphere rotating around Earth (Figure 2.9). From this perspective you can see how the universe seems to turn around us: Every object on the celestial sphere appears to make a simple daily circle around Earth. However, the motion can look a little more complex in the local sky, because the horizon cuts the celestial sphere in half. Figure 2.10 shows the idea for a location in the United States. If you study the figure carefully, you'll notice the following key facts about the paths of various stars (and other celestial objects) through the local sky:

- Stars relatively near the north celestial pole remain perpetually above the horizon. They never rise or set but instead make daily counterclockwise circles around the north celestial pole. We say that such stars are **circumpolar**.

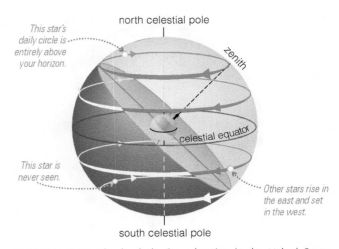

FIGURE 2.10 The local sky for a location in the United States (40°N). The horizon slices through the celestial sphere at an angle to the equator, causing the daily circles of stars to appear tilted in the local sky. Note: It may be easier to follow the star paths in the local sky if you rotate the page so that the zenith points up.

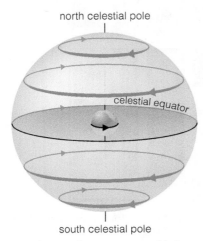

FIGURE 2.9 Earth rotates from west to east (black arrow), making the celestial sphere *appear* to rotate around us from east to west (red arrows).

- Stars relatively near the south celestial pole never rise above the horizon at all.

- All other stars have daily circles that are partly above the horizon and partly below it. Because Earth rotates from west to east (counterclockwise as viewed from above the North Pole), the stars appear to rise in the east and set in the west.

The time-exposure photograph that opens this chapter (p. 26) shows a part of the daily paths of stars. It was taken at Arches National Park in Utah. Paths of circumpolar stars are visible within the arch; notice that the complete daily circles for these stars are above the horizon (although the photo shows only a portion of each circle). The north celestial pole lies at the center of these circles. The circles grow larger for stars farther from the north celestial pole. If they are large enough, the circles cross the horizon, so that the stars rise in the east and set in the west. The same ideas apply in the Southern Hemisphere, except that circumpolar stars are those near the south celestial pole.

Why do the constellations we see depend on latitude and time of year?

If you stay in one place, the basic patterns of motion in the sky will stay the same from one night to the next. However, if you travel far north or south, you'll see a different set of constellations than you see at home. And even if you stay in one place, you'll see different constellations at different times of year. Let's explore why.

Variation with Latitude To understand why the visible constellations vary with northward or southward travel, we must review how we locate points on Earth (Figure 2.11a). **Latitude** measures north-south position; it is defined to be 0° at the equator, increasing to 90°N at the North Pole and 90°S at the South Pole. Note that "lines of latitude" are actually *circles* running parallel to the equator. **Longitude** measures east-west position, so "lines of longitude" are semicircles (half-circles) extending from the North Pole to the South Pole. By international treaty, longitude is defined to be 0° along the **prime meridian**, which passes through Greenwich, England (Figure 2.11b). Stating a latitude and a longitude pinpoints a location on Earth. For example, Miami lies at about 26°N latitude and 80°W longitude.

Latitude affects the constellations we see because it affects the locations of the horizon and zenith relative to the celestial sphere. Figure 2.12 shows how this works for the latitudes of the North Pole (90°N) and Sydney, Australia (34°S). Note

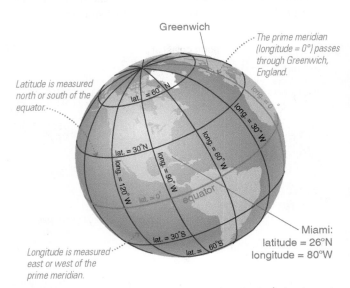

a We can locate any place on Earth's surface by its latitude and longitude.

FIGURE 2.11 Definitions of latitude and longitude.

b The entrance to the Old Royal Greenwich Observatory, near London. The line emerging from the door marks the prime meridian.

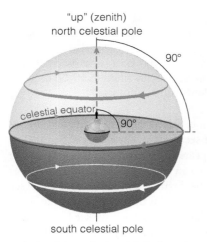

"up" (zenith)
north celestial pole

90°

celestial equator

90°

south celestial pole

a The local sky at the North Pole (latitude 90°N).

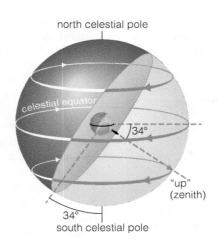

north celestial pole

celestial equator

34°

"up" (zenith)

34°

south celestial pole

b The local sky at latitude 34°S.

FIGURE 2.12 The sky varies with latitude. Notice that the altitude of the celestial pole that is visible in your sky is always equal to your latitude.

that although the sky varies with latitude, it does *not* vary with longitude. For example, Charleston (South Carolina) and San Diego (California) are at about the same latitude, so people in both cities see the same set of constellations at night.

You can learn more about how the sky varies with latitude by studying diagrams like those in Figures 2.10 and 2.12. For example, at the North Pole, you can see only objects that lie on the northern half of the celestial sphere, and they are all circumpolar. That is why the Sun remains above the horizon for 6 months at the North Pole: The Sun lies north of the celestial equator for half of each year (see the yellow dots in Figure 2.3), so during these 6 months, it circles the sky at the North Pole just like a circumpolar star.

The diagrams also show a fact that is very important to navigation:

The altitude of the celestial pole in your sky is equal to your latitude.

For example, if you see the north celestial pole at an altitude of 40° above your north horizon, your latitude is 40°N. Similarly, if you see the south celestial pole at an altitude of 34° above your south horizon, your latitude is 34°S. You can therefore determine your latitude simply by finding the celestial pole in your sky (Figure 2.13). Finding the north celestial pole is fairly easy, because it lies very close to the star Polaris, also known as the North Star (Figure 2.13a). In the Southern

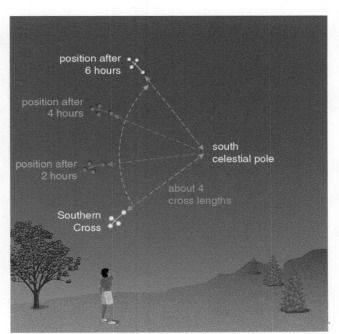

looking northward in the Northern Hemisphere

looking southward in the Southern Hemisphere

a The pointer stars of the Big Dipper point to the North Star, Polaris, which lies within 1° of the north celestial pole. The sky appears to turn *counterclockwise* around the north celestial pole.

b The Southern Cross points to the south celestial pole, which is not marked by any bright star. The sky appears to turn *clockwise* around the south celestial pole.

FIGURE 2.13 Interactive Figure You can determine your latitude by measuring the altitude of the celestial pole in your sky.

Hemisphere, you can find the south celestial pole with the aid of the Southern Cross (Figure 2.13b). We'll discuss celestial navigation and how the sky varies with latitude in more detail in Chapter S1.

Variation with Time of Year   The night sky changes throughout the year because of Earth's changing position in its orbit around the Sun. Figure 2.14 shows how this works. As we orbit the Sun over the course of a year, the Sun *appears* to move against the background of the distant stars in the constellations. We don't see the Sun and the stars at the same time, but if we could we'd notice the Sun gradually moving eastward along the ecliptic, completing one circuit each year. The constellations along the ecliptic are called the **constellations** of the **zodiac**. (Tradition places 12 constellations along the zodiac, but the official borders include a wide swath of a thirteenth constellation, Ophiuchus.)

The Sun's apparent location along the ecliptic determines which constellations we see at night. For example, Figure 2.14 shows that the Sun appears to be in Leo in late August. We therefore cannot see Leo in late August, because it moves with the Sun through the daytime sky. However, we can see Aquarius all night long, since it is opposite Leo on the celestial sphere. Six months later, in February, we see Leo at night while Aquarius is above the horizon only in the daytime.

COMMON MISCONCEPTIONS

What Makes the North Star Special?

Most people are aware that the North Star, Polaris, is a special star. Contrary to a relatively common belief, however, it is *not* the brightest star in the sky. More than 50 other stars are just as bright or brighter. Polaris is special not because of its brightness, but because it is so close to the north celestial pole and therefore very useful in navigation.

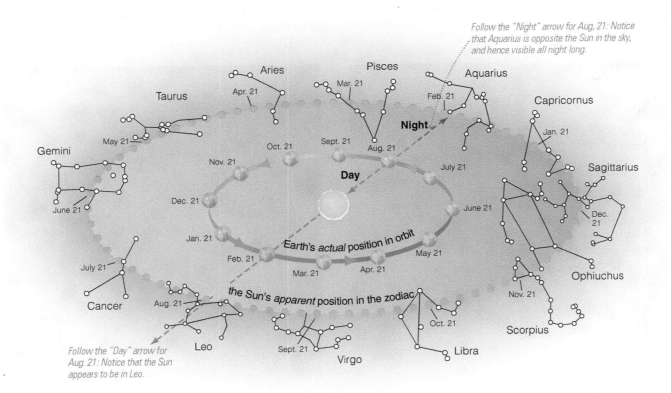

Follow the "Night" arrow for Aug, 21: Notice that Aquarius is opposite the Sun in the sky, and hence visible all night long.

Follow the "Day" arrow for Aug. 21: Notice that the Sun appears to be in Leo.

FIGURE 2.14 Interactive Figure   The Sun appears to move steadily eastward along the ecliptic as Earth orbits the Sun, so we see the Sun against the background of different zodiac constellations at different times of year. For example, on August 21 the Sun appears to be in Leo, because it is between us and the much more distant stars that make up Leo.

2.2 THE REASON FOR SEASONS

We have seen how Earth's rotation makes the sky appear to circle us daily and how the night sky changes as Earth orbits the Sun each year. The combination of Earth's rotation and orbit also leads to the progression of the seasons. In this section, we'll explore the reason for seasons.

What causes the seasons?

You know that we have seasonal changes, such as longer and warmer days in summer and shorter and cooler days in winter. But why do the seasons occur? The answer is that the tilt of Earth's axis causes sunlight to fall differently on Earth at different times of year.

Figure 2.15 illustrates the key ideas. Step 1 shows that Earth's axis remains pointed in the same direction in space (toward Polaris) throughout the year. As a result, the orientation of the axis *relative to the Sun* changes over the course of each orbit: The Northern Hemisphere is tipped toward the Sun in June and away from the Sun in December, while the reverse is true for the Southern Hemisphere. That is why the two hemispheres experience opposite seasons. The rest of the figure shows how the changing angle of sunlight on the two hemispheres leads directly to seasons.

Step 2 shows Earth in June, when axis tilt causes sunlight to strike the Northern Hemisphere at a steeper angle and the Southern Hemisphere at a shallower angle. The steeper sunlight angle makes it summer in the Northern Hemisphere for two reasons. First, as shown in the zoom-out, the steeper angle means more concentrated sunlight, which tends to make it warmer. Second, if you visualize what happens as Earth rotates each day, you'll see that the steeper angle also means the Sun follows a longer and higher path through the sky, giving the Northern Hemisphere more hours of daylight during which it is warmed by the Sun. The opposite is true for the Southern Hemisphere at this time: The shallower sunlight angle makes it winter there because sunlight is less concentrated and the Sun follows a shorter, lower path through the sky.

The sunlight angle gradually changes as Earth orbits the Sun. At the opposite side of Earth's orbit, Step 4 shows that it has become winter for the Northern Hemisphere and summer for the Southern Hemisphere. In between these two extremes, Step 3 shows that both hemispheres are illuminated equally in March and September. It is therefore spring for the hemisphere that is on the way from winter to summer, and fall for the hemisphere on the way from summer to winter.

Notice that the seasons on Earth are caused only by the axis tilt and *not* by any change in Earth's distance from the Sun. Although Earth's orbital distance varies over the course of each year, the variation is fairly small: Earth is only about 3% farther from the Sun at its farthest point than at its nearest. The difference in the strength of sunlight due to this small change in distance is easily overwhelmed by the effects caused by the axis tilt. If Earth did not have an axis tilt, we would not have seasons.

THINK ABOUT IT

Jupiter has an axis tilt of about 3°, small enough to be insignificant. Saturn has an axis tilt of about 27°, slightly greater than that of Earth. Both planets have nearly circular orbits around the Sun. Do you expect Jupiter to have seasons? Do you expect Saturn to have seasons? Explain.

Solstices and Equinoxes To help us mark the changing seasons, we define four special moments in the year, each of which corresponds to one of the four special positions in Earth's orbit shown in Figure 2.15.

- The **summer (June) solstice**, which occurs around June 21, is the moment when the Northern Hemisphere is tipped most directly toward the Sun (and the Southern Hemisphere is tipped most directly away).

- The **winter (December) solstice**, which occurs around December 21, is the moment when the Northern Hemisphere is tipped most directly away from the Sun (and the Southern Hemisphere is tipped most directly toward it).

- The **spring (March) equinox**, which occurs around March 21, is the moment when the Northern Hemisphere goes from being tipped slightly away from the Sun to being tipped slightly toward the Sun.

- The **fall (September) equinox**, which occurs around September 22, is the moment when the Northern Hemisphere first starts to be tipped away from the Sun.

The exact dates and times of the solstices and equinoxes vary from year to year, but stay within a couple of days of the dates given here. In fact, our modern calendar includes leap years in a pattern specifically designed to keep the solstices and equinoxes around the same dates [Section S1.1].

Ancient people recognized the days on which the solstices and equinoxes occurred by observing the Sun in the sky. Many ancient structures were used for this purpose, including Stonehenge in England and the Sun Dagger in New Mexico [Section 3.1].

COMMON MISCONCEPTIONS

The Cause of Seasons

Many people guess that seasons are caused by variations in Earth's distance from the Sun. But if this were true, the whole Earth would have to have summer or winter at the same time, and it doesn't: The seasons are opposite in the Northern and Southern Hemispheres. In fact, Earth's slightly varying orbital distance has virtually no effect on the weather. The real cause of the seasons is Earth's axis tilt, which causes the two hemispheres to take turns being tipped toward the Sun over the course of each year.

Earth's seasons are caused by the tilt of its rotation axis, which is why the seasons are opposite in the two hemispheres. The seasons do *not* depend on Earth's distance from the Sun, which varies only slightly throughout the year.

(1) **Axis Tilt:** Earth's axis points in the same direction throughout the year, which causes changes in Earth's orientation *relative to the Sun*.

(2) **Northern Summer/Southern Winter:** In June, sunlight falls more directly on the Northern Hemisphere, which makes it summer there because solar energy is more concentrated and the Sun follows a longer and higher path through the sky. The Southern Hemisphere receives less direct sunlight, making it winter.

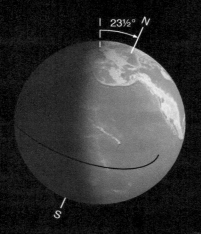

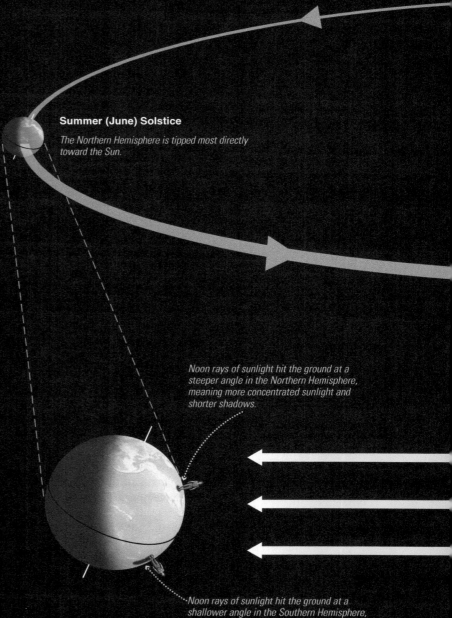

Summer (June) Solstice

The Northern Hemisphere is tipped most directly toward the Sun.

Noon rays of sunlight hit the ground at a steeper angle in the Northern Hemisphere, meaning more concentrated sunlight and shorter shadows.

Noon rays of sunlight hit the ground at a shallower angle in the Southern Hemisphere, meaning less concentrated sunlight and longer shadows.

Interpreting the Diagram

To interpret the seasons diagram properly, keep in mind:

1. Earth's size relative to its orbit would be microscopic on this scale, meaning that both hemispheres are at essentially the same distance from the Sun.

2. The diagram is a side view of Earth's orbit. A top-down view (below) shows that Earth orbits in a nearly perfect circle and comes closest to the Sun in January.

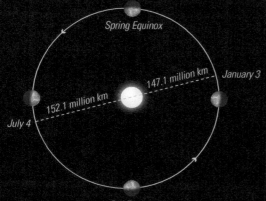

Spring Equinox

147.1 million km   January 3

152.1 million km

July 4

Fall Equinox

③ Spring/Fall: Spring and fall begin when sunlight falls equally on both hemispheres, which happens twice a year: In March, when spring begins in the Northern Hemisphere and fall in the Southern Hemisphere; and in September, when fall begins in the Northern Hemisphere and spring in the Southern Hemisphere.

④ Northern Winter/Southern Summer: In December, sunlight falls less directly on the Northern Hemisphere, which makes it winter because solar energy is less concentrated and the Sun follows a shorter and lower path through the sky. The Southern Hemisphere receives more direct sunlight, making it summer.

Spring (March) Equinox

The Sun shines equally on both hemispheres.

The variation in Earth's orientation relative to the Sun means that the seasons are linked to four special points in Earth's orbit:

***Solstices** are the two points at which sunlight becomes most extreme for the two hemispheres.*

***Equinoxes** are the two points at which the hemispheres are equally illuminated.*

Winter (December) Solstice

The Southern Hemisphere is tipped most directly toward the Sun.

Fall (September) Equinox

The Sun shines equally on both hemispheres.

Noon rays of sunlight hit the ground at a shallower angle in the Northern Hemisphere, meaning less concentrated sunlight and longer shadows.

Noon rays of sunlight hit the ground at a steeper angle in the Southern Hemisphere, meaning more concentrated sunlight and shorter shadows.

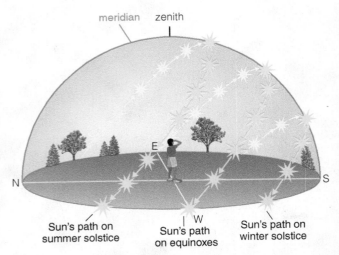

meridian zenith

N E W S

Sun's path on summer solstice

Sun's path on equinoxes

Sun's path on winter solstice

FIGURE 2.16 Interactive Figure This diagram shows the Sun's path on the solstices and equinoxes for a Northern Hemisphere sky (latitude 40°N). The precise paths are different for other latitudes. Notice that the Sun rises exactly due east and sets exactly due west only on the equinoxes.

The equinoxes occur on the only two days of the year on which the Sun rises precisely due east and sets precisely due west (Figure 2.16). These are also the only two days when sunlight falls equally on both hemispheres. The summer solstice occurs on the day that the Sun follows its longest and highest path through the Northern Hemisphere sky (and its shortest and lowest path through the Southern Hemisphere sky). It is therefore the day on which the Sun rises and sets farther to the north than on any other day of the year, and on which the noon Sun reaches its highest point in the Northern Hemisphere sky. The opposite is true on the day of the winter solstice, when the Sun rises and sets farthest to the south and the noon Sun is lower in the Northern Hemisphere sky than on any other day of the year. Figure 2.17 shows how the Sun's midday altitude varies over the course of the year.

First Days of Seasons We usually say that each equinox and solstice marks the first day of a season. For example, the day of the summer solstice is usually called the "first day of summer." Notice, however, that the summer solstice occurs when the Northern Hemisphere has its *maximum* tilt toward the Sun. You might then wonder why we consider the summer solstice to be the beginning rather than the midpoint of summer.

Although the choice of the summer solstice as the "first" day of summer is somewhat arbitrary, it makes sense in at least two ways. First, it was much easier for ancient people to identify the days on which the Sun reached extreme positions in the sky—such as when it reached its highest point on the summer solstice—than other days in between. Second, we usually think of the seasons in terms of weather, and the solstices and equinoxes correspond quite well with the beginnings of seasonal weather patterns. For example, although the Sun's path through the Northern Hemisphere sky is longest and highest around the time of the summer solstice, the warmest days tend to come 1 to 2 months later. To understand why, think about what happens when you heat a pot of cold

FIGURE 2.17 This composite photograph shows midday images of the Sun at 7- to 11-day intervals over the course of a year, always from the same spot (the Parthenon in Athens, Greece) and at the same time of day (technically, at the same "mean solar time"). Notice the dramatic change in the Sun's midday altitude over the course of the year. We'll discuss the reasons for the "figure 8" (called an *analemma*) in Chapter S1.

soup. Even though you may have the stove turned on high from the start, it takes a while for the soup to warm up. In the same way, it takes some time for sunlight to heat the ground and oceans from the cold of winter to the warmth of summer. "Midsummer" in terms of weather therefore comes in late July and early August, which makes the summer solstice a pretty good choice for the "first day of summer." For similar reasons, the winter solstice is a good choice for the first day of winter, and the spring and fall equinoxes are good choices for the first days of those seasons.

Seasons Around the World Notice that the names of the solstices and equinoxes reflect the northern seasons, and therefore sound backward to people who live in the Southern Hemisphere. For example, Southern Hemisphere winter begins when Earth is at the orbital point usually called the *summer* solstice. This apparent injustice to people in the Southern Hemisphere arose because the solstices and equinoxes were named long ago by people living in the Northern Hemisphere. A similar injustice is inflicted on people living in equatorial

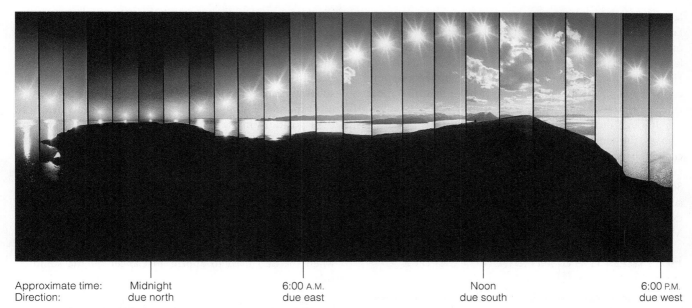

Approximate time:	Midnight	6:00 A.M.	Noon	6:00 P.M.
Direction:	due north	due east	due south	due west

FIGURE 2.18 This sequence of photos shows the progression of the Sun all the way around the horizon on the summer solstice at the Arctic Circle. Notice that the Sun does not set but instead skims the northern horizon at midnight. It then gradually rises higher, reaching its highest point at noon, when it appears due south.

regions. If you study Figure 2.14 carefully, you'll see that Earth's equator gets its most direct sunlight on the two equinoxes and its least direct sunlight on the solstices, so people living near the equator don't experience four seasons in the same way as people living at mid-latitudes. Instead, equatorial regions generally have rainy and dry seasons, with the rainy seasons coming when the Sun is higher in the sky.

In addition, seasonal variations around the times of the solstices are more extreme at high latitudes. For example, Vermont has much longer summer days and much longer winter nights than Florida. At the Arctic Circle (latitude $66\frac{1}{2}°$) the Sun remains above the horizon all day long on the summer solstice (Figure 2.18), and below the horizon on the winter solstice. The most extreme cases occur at the North and South Poles, where the Sun remains above the horizon for 6 months in summer and below the horizon for 6 months in winter.*

---

*These statements are true for the Sun's *real* position, but the bending of light by Earth's atmosphere makes the Sun *appear* to be about 0.6° higher than it really is when it is near the horizon.

Why Orbital Distance Doesn't Affect Our Seasons

We've seen that the seasons are caused by Earth's axis tilt, not by Earth's slightly varying distance from the Sun. Still, we might expect the varying orbital distance to play at least some role. For example, because the Northern Hemisphere has winter when Earth is closer to the Sun and summer when Earth is farther away (see the lower left diagram in Figure 2.15), we might expect the Northern Hemisphere to have more moderate seasons than the Southern Hemisphere. In fact, weather records show that the opposite is true: Northern Hemisphere seasons are slightly more extreme than those of the Southern Hemisphere.

The main reason for this surprising fact becomes obvious when you look at a map of Earth (Figure 2.19). Most of Earth's land lies in the Northern Hemisphere, with far more ocean in the Southern Hemisphere. As you'll notice at any beach, lake, or pool, water takes longer to heat or cool than soil or rock (largely because sunlight heats bodies of water to a depth of many meters while heating only the very top

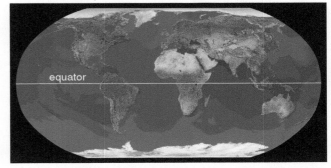

FIGURE 2.19 Most land lies in the Northern Hemisphere while most ocean lies in the Southern Hemisphere. The climate-moderating effects of water make Southern Hemisphere seasons less extreme than Northern Hemisphere seasons.

layer of land). The water temperature therefore remains fairly steady both day and night, while the ground can heat up and cool down dramatically. The Southern Hemisphere's larger amount of ocean moderates its climate. The Northern Hemisphere, with more land and less ocean, heats up and cools down more easily, which is why it has the more extreme seasons.

Although distance from the Sun plays no role in Earth's seasons, the same is not always true for other planets, especially if they have significantly greater distance variations. For example, Mars is more than 20% closer to the Sun during its Southern Hemisphere summer than its Northern Hemisphere summer. This gives its Southern Hemisphere much more extreme seasons than its Northern Hemisphere, even though Mars has nearly the same axis tilt as Earth.

How does the orientation of Earth's axis change with time?

We have now discussed both daily and seasonal changes in the sky, but there are other changes that occur over longer periods of time. One of the most important of these slow changes is called **precession**, a gradual wobble that alters the orientation of Earth's axis in space.

Precession occurs with many rotating objects. You can see it easily by spinning a top (Figure 2.20a). As the top spins rapidly, you'll notice that its axis sweeps out a circle at a somewhat slower rate. We say that the top's axis *precesses*. Earth's axis precesses in much the same way, but far more slowly (Figure 2.20b). Each cycle of Earth's precession takes about 26,000 years, gradually changing where the axis points in space. Today, the axis points toward Polaris, making it our North Star. Some 13,000 years from now, Vega will be the star

closest to true north. At most other times, the axis does not point near any bright star.

Notice that precession does not change the *amount* of the axis tilt (which stays close to $23\frac{1}{2}°$) and therefore does not affect the pattern of the seasons. However, because the solstices and equinoxes correspond to points in Earth's orbit that depend on the direction the axis points in space, their positions in the orbit gradually shift with the cycle of precession. As a result, the constellations associated with the solstices and equinoxes gradually change. For example, a couple thousand years ago the Sun appeared in the constellation Cancer on the day of the summer solstice, but it now appears in Gemini on that day. This explains something you can see on any world map: The latitude at which the Sun is directly overhead on the summer solstice ($23\frac{1}{2}°$N) is called the *Tropic of Cancer,* telling us that it got its name back when the Sun used to appear in Cancer on the summer solstice.

Why does precession occur? It is caused by gravity's effect on a tilted, rotating object that is *not* a perfect sphere. You have probably seen how gravity affects a top. If you try to balance a nonspinning top on its point, it will fall over almost immediately. This happens because a top that is not spherical will inevitably lean a little to one side. No matter how slight this lean, gravity will quickly tip the nonspinning top over. However, if you spin the top rapidly, it does not fall over so

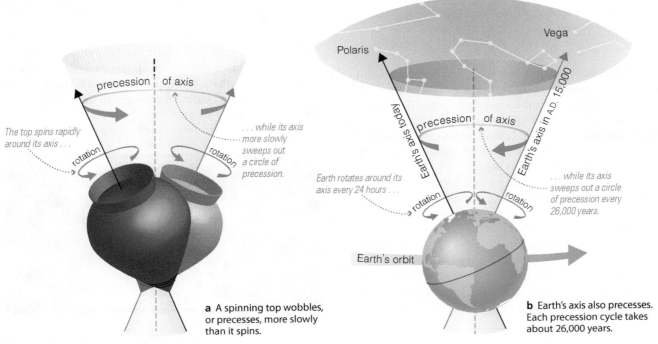

a A spinning top wobbles, or precesses, more slowly than it spins.

b Earth's axis also precesses. Each precession cycle takes about 26,000 years.

FIGURE 2.20 Interactive Figure Precession affects the orientation of a spinning object's axis but not the amount of its tilt.

Sun Signs

You probably know your astrological "Sun sign." When astrology began a few thousand years ago, your Sun sign was supposed to represent the constellation in which the Sun appeared on your birth date. However, because of precession, this is no longer the case for most people. For example, if your birthday is March 21, your Sun sign is Aries even though the Sun now appears in Pisces on that date. The problem is that astrological Sun signs are based on the positions of the Sun among the stars as they were almost 2000 years ago. Because Earth's axis has moved about 1/13 of the way through its 26,000-year precession cycle since that time, the Sun signs are off by nearly a month from the actual positions of the Sun among the constellations today.

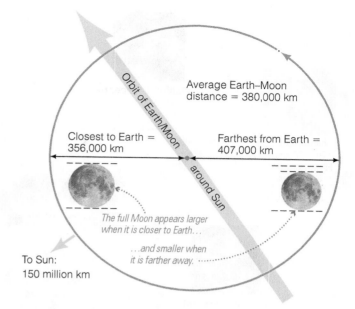

FIGURE 2.21 The Moon's orbit around Earth, shown on the 1-to-10-billion scale used in Section 1.2 (see Figure 1.6). The segment shown of our orbit around the Sun looks nearly straight because the distance to the Sun is so great compared to the size of the Moon's orbit. The inset photos contrast the relative angular sizes of the full moon in our sky when the Moon is at the near and far points of its orbit; of course, full moon occurs only when the Moon is opposite the Sun as seen from Earth.

easily. The spinning top stays upright because rotating objects tend to keep spinning around the same rotation axis (a consequence of the *law of conservation of angular momentum* [Section 4.3]). This tendency prevents gravity from immediately pulling the spinning top over, since falling over would mean a change in the spin axis from near-vertical to horizontal. Instead, gravity succeeds only in making the axis trace circles of precession. As friction slows the top's spin, the circles of precession get wider and wider, and ultimately the top falls over. If there were no friction to slow its spin, the top would spin and precess forever.

The spinning (rotating) Earth precesses because of gravitational tugs from the Sun and Moon. Earth is not quite a perfect sphere, instead bulging slightly at its equator. Because the equator is tilted $23\frac{1}{2}°$ to the ecliptic plane, the gravitational attractions of the Sun and Moon try to pull the equatorial bulge into the ecliptic plane, effectively trying to "straighten out" Earth's axis tilt. However, like the spinning top, Earth tends to keep rotating around the same axis. Gravity therefore does not succeed in changing Earth's axis tilt and instead only makes the axis precess. If you want to gain a better understanding of precession and how it works, you might wish to experiment with a simple toy *gyroscope*. Gyroscopes are essentially rotating wheels mounted in a way that allows them to move freely, which makes it easy to see how their spin rate affects their motion. (The fact that gyroscopes tend to keep the same rotation axis makes them very useful in aircraft and spacecraft navigation.)

(MA) **Phases of the Moon Tutorial, Lessons 1–3**

2.3 THE MOON, OUR CONSTANT COMPANION

Aside from the Sun, the Moon is the brightest and most noticeable object in our sky. The Moon is our constant companion in space, orbiting Earth about once every $27\frac{1}{3}$ days.

Figure 2.21 shows the Moon's orbit on the same scale we used for the model solar system in Section 1.2. Remember that on this scale, the Sun is about the size of a large grapefruit and is located about 15 meters from Earth. The entire orbit of the Moon would fit easily inside the Sun, and for practical purposes we can consider Earth and the Moon to share the same orbit around the Sun.

Like all objects in space, the Moon appears to reside on the celestial sphere. Earth's daily rotation makes the Moon appear to rise in the east and set in the west each day. In addition, because of its orbit around Earth, the Moon appears to move eastward from night to night through the constellations of the zodiac. Each circuit through the constellations takes the same $27\frac{1}{3}$ days that the Moon takes to orbit Earth. If you do the math, you'll see that this means the Moon moves relative to the stars by about $\frac{1}{2}°$—its own angular size—each hour. You can notice this gradual motion in just a few hours by checking the Moon's position compared to bright stars near it in the sky.

Why do we see phases of the Moon?

As the Moon moves through the sky, both its appearance and the times at which it rises and sets change with the cycle of **lunar phases**. The phase of the Moon on any given day depends on its position relative to the Sun as it orbits Earth.

The easiest way to understand the lunar phases is with the simple demonstration illustrated in Figure 2.22. Take a ball outside on a sunny day. (If it's dark or cloudy, you can use a flashlight instead of the Sun; put the flashlight on a table a few meters away and shine it toward you.) Hold the ball at arm's length to represent the Moon while your head represents Earth. Slowly spin around (counterclockwise), so that the ball goes around you just as the Moon orbits Earth. As you turn, you'll see the ball go through phases just like

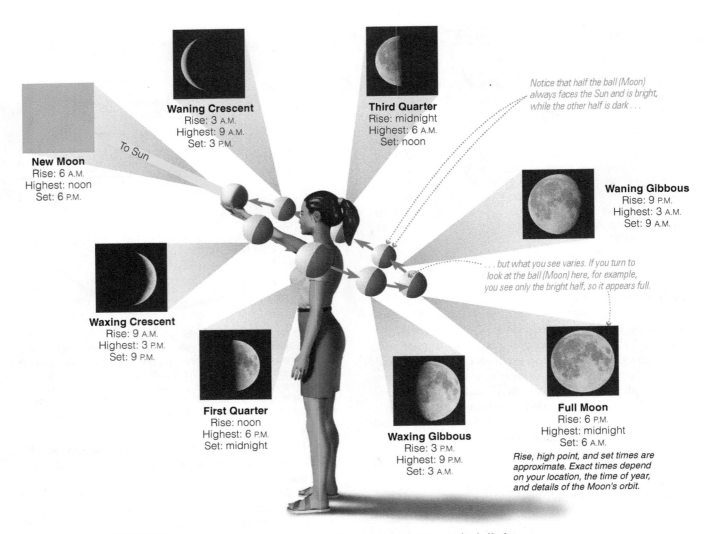

Waning Crescent
Rise: 3 A.M.
Highest: 9 A.M.
Set: 3 P.M.

Third Quarter
Rise: midnight
Highest: 6 A.M.
Set: noon

New Moon
Rise: 6 A.M.
Highest: noon
Set: 6 P.M.

To Sun

Waning Gibbous
Rise: 9 P.M.
Highest: 3 A.M.
Set: 9 A.M.

Waxing Crescent
Rise: 9 A.M.
Highest: 3 P.M.
Set: 9 P.M.

. . . but what you see varies. If you turn to look at the ball (Moon) here, for example, you see only the bright half, so it appears full.

First Quarter
Rise: noon
Highest: 6 P.M.
Set: midnight

Waxing Gibbous
Rise: 3 P.M.
Highest: 9 P.M.
Set: 3 A.M.

Full Moon
Rise: 6 P.M.
Highest: midnight
Set: 6 A.M.

Rise, high point, and set times are approximate. Exact times depend on your location, the time of year, and details of the Moon's orbit.

FIGURE 2.22 Interactive Figure. A simple demonstration illustrates the phases of the Moon. The half of the ball (Moon) facing the Sun is always illuminated while the half facing away is always dark, but you see the ball go through phases as it orbits around your head (Earth). (The new moon photo shows blue sky, because a new moon is always close to the Sun in the sky and hence hidden from view by the bright light of the Sun.)

the Moon. If you think about what's happening, you'll realize that the phases of the ball result from just two basic facts:

1. Half the ball always faces the Sun (or flashlight) and therefore is bright, while the other half faces away from the Sun and therefore is dark.

2. As you look at the ball at different positions in its "orbit" around your head, you see different combinations of its bright and dark faces.

For example, when you hold the ball directly opposite the Sun, you see only the bright portion of the ball, which represents the "full" phase. When you hold the ball at its "first-quarter" position, half the face you see is dark and the other half is bright.

We see lunar phases for the same reason. Half the Moon is always illuminated by the Sun, but the amount of this illuminated half that we see from Earth depends on the Moon's position in its orbit. The photographs in Figure 2.22 show how the phases look. Each complete cycle of phases, from one new moon to the next, takes about $29\frac{1}{2}$ days—hence the

origin of the word *month* (think "moonth"). This is about 2 days longer than the Moon's actual orbital period because of Earth's motion around the Sun during the time the Moon is orbiting around Earth (see Figure S1.3).

The Moon's phase is directly related to the time it rises, reaches its highest point in the sky, and sets. For example, the full moon must rise around sunset, because it occurs when the Moon is opposite the Sun in the sky. It therefore reaches its highest point in the sky at midnight and sets around sunrise. Similarly, a first-quarter moon must rise around noon, reach its highest point around 6 p.m., and set around midnight, because it occurs when the Moon is about 90° east of the Sun in our sky. Figure 2.22 lists the approximate rise, highest point, and set times for each phase.

THINK ABOUT IT

*S*uppose you go outside in the morning and notice that the visible face of the Moon is half-light and half-dark. Is this a first-quarter or third-quarter moon? How do you know?

Notice that the phases from new to full are said to be *waxing*, which means "increasing." Phases from full to new are *waning*, or "decreasing." Also notice that no phase is called a "half moon." Instead, we see half the Moon's face at first-quarter and third-quarter phases; these phases mark the times when the Moon is one-quarter or three-quarters of the way through its monthly cycle (which begins at new moon). The phases just before and after new moon are called *crescent*, while those just before and after full moon are called *gibbous* (pronounced with a hard *g* as in "gift"). A gibbous moon is essentially the opposite of a crescent moon—a crescent moon has a small sliver of light while a gibbous moon has a small sliver of dark. The term *gibbous* literally means "hump-backed," so you can see how the gibbous moon gets its name.

The Moon's Synchronous Rotation Although we see many *phases* of the Moon, we do not see many *faces*. In fact, from Earth we always see the same face of the Moon.* This happens because the Moon rotates on its axis in the same amount of time that it takes to orbit Earth, a trait called **synchronous rotation**. A simple demonstration shows the idea. Place a ball on a table to represent Earth while you represent the Moon. Start by facing the ball. If you do not rotate as you walk around the ball, you'll be looking away from it by the time you are halfway around your orbit (Figure 2.23a). The only way you can face the ball at all times is by completing exactly one rotation while you complete one orbit (Figure 2.23b). Note that the Moon's synchronous rotation is *not* a coincidence; rather, it is a consequence of Earth's gravity affecting the Moon in much the same way that the Moon's gravity causes tides on Earth [Section 4.5].

The View from the Moon A good way to solidify your understanding of the lunar phases is to imagine that you live on the side of the Moon that faces Earth. For example,

---

*Because the Moon's orbital speed varies while its rotation rate is steady, the visible face appears to wobble slightly back and forth as the Moon orbits Earth. This effect, called *libration*, allows us to see a total of about 59% of the Moon's surface over the course of a month, even though we see only 50% of the Moon at any single time.

The "Dark Side" of the Moon

The phrase *dark side of the Moon* really should be used to mean the night side—that is, the side facing away from the Sun. Unfortunately, *dark side* traditionally meant what would better be called the *far side*—the face that never can be seen from Earth. Many people still refer to the far side as the "dark side," even though it is not necessarily dark. For example, during new moon the far side faces the Sun and hence is completely sunlit. The only time the far side is completely dark is at full moon, when it faces away from both the Sun and Earth.

what would you see if you looked at Earth when people on Earth saw a new moon? By remembering that a new moon occurs when the Moon is between the Sun and Earth, you'll realize that from the Moon you'd be looking at Earth's daytime side and hence would see a *full earth*. Similarly, at full moon you would be facing the night side of Earth and would see a *new earth*. In general, you'd always see Earth in a phase opposite the phase of the Moon seen by people on Earth at the same time. Moreover, because the Moon always shows nearly the same face to Earth, Earth would appear to hang nearly stationary in your sky as it went through its cycle of phases.

THINK ABOUT IT

About how long would each day and night last if you lived on the Moon? Explain.

Thinking about the view from the Moon clarifies another interesting feature of the lunar phases: The dark portion of the lunar face is not *totally* dark. Imagine that you are standing on the Moon when it is in a crescent phase. Because it's nearly new moon as seen from Earth, you would see nearly full earth in your sky. Just as we can see at night by the light of the Moon, the light of Earth would illuminate your night moonscape. In fact, because Earth is much larger than the Moon, the full earth is much bigger and brighter in the lunar

a If you do not rotate while walking around the model, you will not always face it.

b You will face the model at all times only if you rotate exactly once during each orbit.

FIGURE 2.23 The fact that we always see the same face of the Moon means that the Moon must rotate once in the same amount of time that it takes to orbit Earth once. You can see why by walking around a model of Earth while imagining that you are the Moon.

sky than the full moon is in Earth's sky. This reflected light from Earth faintly illuminates the "dark" portion of the Moon's face. It is often called the *ashen light* or *earthshine* and it enables us to see the outline of the full face of the Moon even when the Moon is not full.

 Eclipses Tutorial, Lessons 1–3

What causes eclipses?

Occasionally, the Moon's orbit around Earth causes events much more dramatic than lunar phases. The Moon and Earth cast shadows in sunlight, and these shadows can create **eclipses** when the Sun, Earth, and Moon fall into a straight line. Eclipses come in two basic types:

- A **lunar eclipse** occurs when Earth lies directly between the Sun and Moon, so that Earth's shadow falls on the Moon.

- A **solar eclipse** occurs when the Moon lies directly between the Sun and Earth, so that the Moon's shadow falls on Earth. People living within the area covered by the Moon's shadow will see the Sun blocked or partially blocked from view.

Conditions for Eclipses Look once more at Figure 2.22. The figure makes it look as if the Sun, Earth, and Moon line up with every new and full moon. If this figure told the whole story of the Moon's orbit, we would have both a lunar and a solar eclipse every month—but we don't.

Moon in the Daytime and Stars on the Moon

In traditions and stories, night is so closely associated with the Moon that many people mistakenly believe that the Moon is visible only in the nighttime sky. In fact, the Moon is above the horizon as often in the daytime as at night, though it is easily visible only when its light is not drowned out by sunlight. For example, a first-quarter moon is easy to spot in the late afternoon as it rises through the eastern sky, and a third-quarter moon is visible in the morning as it heads toward the western horizon.

Another misconception appears in illustrations that show a star in the dark portion of the crescent moon. The star in the dark portion appears to be in front of the Moon, which is impossible because the Moon is much closer to us than is any star.

The missing piece of the story in Figure 2.22 is that the Moon's orbit is slightly inclined (by about 5°) to the ecliptic plane (the plane of Earth's orbit around the Sun). To visualize this inclination, imagine the ecliptic plane as the surface of a pond, as shown in Figure 2.24. Because of the inclination of its orbit, the Moon spends most of its time either above or below this surface. It crosses *through* this surface only twice during each orbit: once coming out and once going back in. The two points in each orbit at which the Moon crosses the surface are called the **nodes** of the Moon's orbit.

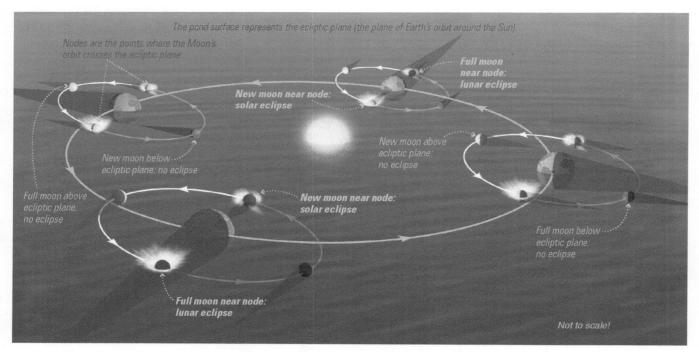

FIGURE 2.24 This illustration represents the ecliptic plane as the surface of a pond. The Moon's orbit is tilted by about 5° to the ecliptic plane, so the Moon spends half of each orbit above the plane (the pond surface) and half below it. Eclipses occur only when the Moon is at both a node (passing through the pond surface) and a phase of either new moon (for a solar eclipse) or full moon (for a lunar eclipse)—as is the case with the lower left and top right orbits shown.

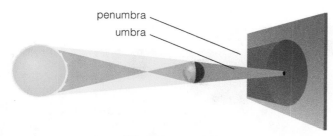

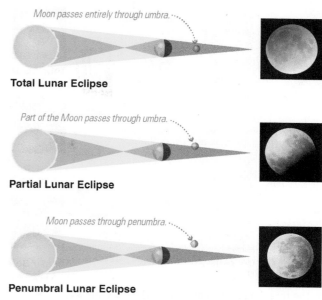

FIGURE 2.25 [Interactive Figure] The shadow cast by an object in sunlight. Sunlight is fully blocked in the umbra and partially blocked in the penumbra.

Notice that the nodes are aligned approximately the same way (diagonally on the page in Figure 2.24) throughout the year, which means they lie along a nearly straight line with the Sun and Earth about twice each year. We therefore find the following conditions for an eclipse to occur:

1. The phase of the Moon must be full (for a lunar eclipse) or new (for a solar eclipse).

2. The new or full moon must occur during one of the periods when the nodes of the Moon's orbit are aligned with the Sun and Earth.

Although there are two basic types of eclipse—lunar and solar—each of these types can look different depending on precisely how the shadows fall. The shadow of the Moon or Earth consists of two distinct regions: a central **umbra**, where sunlight is completely blocked, and a surrounding **penumbra**, where sunlight is only partially blocked (Figure 2.25). Therefore, an umbral shadow is totally dark, while a penumbral shadow is only slightly darker than no shadow. Let's see how this affects eclipses.

Lunar Eclipses A lunar eclipse begins at the moment when the Moon's orbit first carries it into Earth's penumbra. After that, we will see one of three types of lunar eclipse (Figure 2.26). If the Sun, Earth, and Moon are nearly perfectly aligned, the Moon passes through Earth's umbra and we see a **total lunar eclipse**. If the alignment is somewhat less perfect, only part of the full moon passes through the umbra (with the rest in the penumbra) and we see a **partial lunar eclipse**. If the Moon passes *only* through Earth's penumbra, we see a **penumbral lunar eclipse**.

Penumbral eclipses are the most common type of lunar eclipse, but they are the least visually impressive because the full moon darkens only slightly. Earth's umbral shadow clearly

Total Lunar Eclipse — *Moon passes entirely through umbra.*

Partial Lunar Eclipse — *Part of the Moon passes through umbra.*

Penumbral Lunar Eclipse — *Moon passes through penumbra.*

FIGURE 2.26 [Interactive Figure] The three types of lunar eclipse.

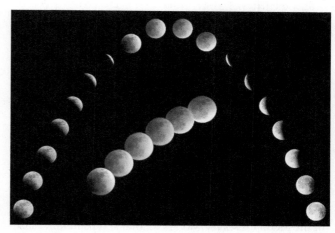

FIGURE 2.27 This sequence of photos, taken at 5-minute intervals, shows the progression of a total lunar eclipse; the central photos show more detail during totality. Notice Earth's curved shadow advancing across the Moon during the partial phases, and the redness of the full moon during totality. The arc-shaped arrangement was chosen for effect and has no inherent meaning.

darkens part of the Moon's face during a partial lunar eclipse, and the curvature of this shadow demonstrates that Earth is round. A total lunar eclipse is particularly spectacular because the Moon becomes dark and eerily red during **totality**—the time during which the Moon is entirely engulfed in the umbra (Figure 2.27). Totality typically lasts about an hour. The Moon becomes dark because it is in shadow, and red because Earth's atmosphere bends some of the red light from the Sun toward the Moon.

Solar Eclipses We can also see three types of solar eclipse (Figure 2.28). If a solar eclipse occurs when the Moon is relatively close to Earth in its orbit, the Moon's umbra touches a small area of Earth's surface (no more than about 270 kilometers in diameter). Within this area you will see a **total solar eclipse**. Surrounding the region of totality is a much larger

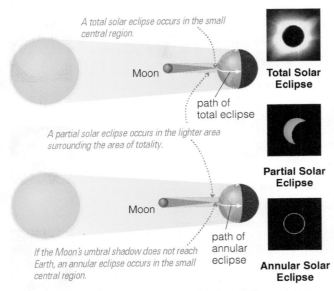

A total solar eclipse occurs in the small central region.

Moon

Total Solar Eclipse

path of total eclipse

A partial solar eclipse occurs in the lighter area surrounding the area of totality.

Moon

Partial Solar Eclipse

path of annular eclipse

If the Moon's umbral shadow does not reach Earth, an annular eclipse occurs in the small central region.

Annular Solar Eclipse

a The three types of solar eclipse. The diagrams show the Moon's shadow falling on Earth; note the dark central umbra surrounded by the much lighter penumbra.

b This photo from Earth orbit shows the Moon's shadow (umbra) on Earth during a total solar elipse. Notice that only a small region of Earth experiences totality at any one time.

FIGURE 2.28 Interactive Figure During a solar eclipse, the Moon's small shadow moves rapidly across the face of Earth.

area (typically about 7000 kilometers in diameter) that falls within the Moon's penumbral shadow. Here you will see a **partial solar eclipse,** in which only part of the Sun is blocked from view. If the eclipse occurs when the Moon is relatively far from Earth in its orbit, the Moon's slightly smaller angular size means its umbral shadow may not quite reach Earth's surface. In that case, you will see an **annular eclipse** in the small region of Earth directly behind the umbra, in which a ring of sunlight surrounds the disk of the Moon. Again, you would see a partial solar eclipse within the surrounding penumbral shadow.

The combination of Earth's rotation and the orbital motion of the Moon causes the Moon's umbral and penumbral shadows to race across the face of Earth at a typical speed of about 1700 kilometers per hour. As a result, the umbral shadow traces a narrow path across Earth, and totality never lasts more than a few minutes in any particular place.

A total solar eclipse is a spectacular sight. It begins when the disk of the Moon first appears to touch the Sun. Over the next couple of hours, the Moon appears to take a larger and larger "bite" out of the Sun. As totality approaches, the sky darkens and temperatures fall. Birds head back to their nests, and crickets begin their nighttime chirping. During the few minutes of totality, the Moon completely blocks the normally visible disk of the Sun, allowing the faint *corona* to be seen (Figure 2.29). The surrounding sky takes on a twilight glow, and planets and bright stars become visible in the daytime. As totality ends, the Sun slowly emerges from behind the Moon over the next couple of hours. However, because your eyes have adapted to the darkness, totality appears to end far more abruptly than it began.

Predicting Eclipses Few phenomena have so inspired and humbled humans throughout the ages as eclipses. For many cultures, eclipses were mystical events associated with

fate or the gods, and countless stories and legends surround them. One legend holds that the Greek philosopher Thales (c. 624–546 B.C.) successfully predicted the year (but presumably not the precise time) that a total eclipse of the Sun would be visible in the area where he lived, which is now part of Turkey. Coincidentally, the eclipse occurred as two opposing armies (the Medes and the Lydians) were massing for battle. The eclipse so frightened the armies that they put down their weapons, signed a treaty, and returned home. Because modern research shows that the only eclipse visible in that part of the world at about that time occurred on May 28, 585 B.C., we know the precise date on which the

FIGURE 2.29 This multiple-exposure photograph shows the progression of a total solar eclipse. Totality (central image) lasts only a few minutes, during which time we can see the faint corona around the outline of the Sun. This photo was taken July 22, 1990, in La Paz, Mexico. The foreground church was photographed at a different time of day.

treaty was signed—the earliest historical event that can be dated precisely.

Much of the mystery of eclipses probably stems from the relative difficulty of predicting them. Look again at Figure 2.24. The two periods each year when the nodes of the Moon's orbit are nearly aligned with the Sun are called **eclipse seasons**. Each eclipse season lasts a few weeks. Some type of lunar eclipse occurs during each eclipse season's full moon, and some type of solar eclipse occurs during its new moon.

If Figure 2.24 told the whole story, eclipse seasons would occur every 6 months and predicting eclipses would be easy. For example, if eclipse seasons always occurred in January and July, eclipses would always occur on the dates of new and full moons in those months. But the figure does not show one important thing about the Moon's orbit: The nodes slowly move around the orbit. As a result, eclipse seasons occur slightly less than 6 months apart (about 173 days apart) and do not recur in the same months year after year.

The combination of the changing dates of eclipse seasons and the $29\frac{1}{2}$-day cycle of lunar phases makes eclipses recur in a cycle of about 18 years $11\frac{1}{3}$ days. This cycle is called the **saros cycle**. Astronomers in many ancient cultures identified the saros cycle and thus could predict *when* eclipses would occur. However, the saros cycle does not account for all the complications involved in predicting eclipses. If a solar eclipse occurred today, the one that would occur 18 years $11\frac{1}{3}$ days from now would not be visible from the same places on Earth and might not be of the same type. For example, one might be total and the other only partial. No ancient culture achieved the ability to predict eclipses in every detail.

Today, we can predict eclipses because we know the precise details of the orbits of Earth and the Moon. Many astronomical software packages, including the *SkyGazer* package that comes with this book, do the necessary calculations automatically. Table 2.1 lists upcoming lunar eclipses; notice that, as we expect, eclipses generally come a little less than 6 months apart. Figure 2.30 shows paths of totality for upcoming total

TABLE 2.1 Lunar Eclipses 2010–2013*

Date	Type	Where You Can See It
June 26, 2010	partial	eastern Asia, Australia, Pacific, western Americas
Dec. 21, 2010	total	eastern Asia, Australia, Pacific, Americas, Europe
June 15, 2011	total	South America, Europe, Africa, Asia, Australia
Dec. 10, 2011	total	Europe, Africa, Asia, Australia, North America
June 4, 2012	partial	Asia, Australia, Americas
Nov. 28, 2012	penumbral	Europe, Africa, Asia, Australia, North America
April 25, 2013	partial	Europe, Africa, Asia, Australia
May 25, 2013	penumbral	Americas, Africa
Oct. 18, 2013	penumbral	Americas, Europe, Africa, Asia

*Dates are based on Universal Time and hence are those in Greenwich, England, at the time of the eclipse; to see an eclipse, check a news source for the exact local time and date. Data from NASA's Eclipse home page maintained by Fred Espenak.

solar eclipses (but not for partial or annular eclipses), using color coding to show eclipses that repeat with the saros cycle.

THINK ABOUT IT

In Table 2.1, notice that there's one exception to the "rule" of eclipses coming a little less than 6 months apart: the 2013 lunar eclipses of April 25 and May 25. How can eclipses occur just a month apart? Should you be surprised that one of these lunar eclipses is penumbral? Explain.

SPECIAL TOPIC

Does the Moon Influence Human Behavior?

From myths of werewolves to stories of romance under the full moon, human culture is filled with claims that our behavior is influenced by the phase of the Moon. Can we say anything scientific about such claims?

The Moon clearly has important influences on Earth. For example, the Moon is primarily responsible for the tides [Section 4.5]. However, the Moon's tidal force cannot directly affect objects as small as people.

If a physical force from the Moon cannot affect human behavior, could we be influenced in other ways? Certainly, anyone who lives near the oceans is influenced by the rising and falling of the tides. For example, fishermen and boaters must follow the tides. Although the Moon does not influence their behavior directly, it does so indirectly through its effect on the oceans.

Physiological patterns in many species appear to follow the lunar phases; for example, some crabs and turtles lay eggs only at full moon. No human trait is so closely linked to lunar phases, but the average human menstrual cycle is so close in length to a lunar month that it is difficult to believe the similarity is mere coincidence. Nevertheless, aside from the physiological cycles and the influence of tides on people who live near the oceans, claims that the lunar phase affects human behavior are difficult to verify scientifically. For example, although it is possible that the full moon brings out certain behaviors, it may also simply be that some behaviors are easier to exhibit when the sky is bright. A beautiful full moon may bring out your desire to walk on the beach under the moonlight, but there is no scientific evidence to suggest that the full moon would affect you the same way if you were confined to a deep cave.

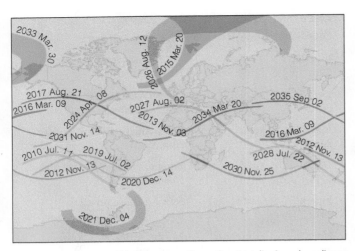

FIGURE 2.30 This map shows the paths of totality for solar eclipses through 2035. Paths of the same color represent eclipses occurring in successive saros cycles, separated by 18 years 11 days. For example, the 2034 eclipse occurs 18 years 11 days after the 2016 eclipse (both shown in red). Eclipse predictions by Fred Espenak; see NASA's Eclipse Web site.

2.4 THE ANCIENT MYSTERY OF THE PLANETS

We've now covered the appearance and motion of the stars, Sun, and Moon in the sky. That leaves us with the planets yet to discuss. As we'll soon see, planetary motion posed an ancient mystery that played a critical role in the development of modern civilization.

Five planets are easy to find with the naked eye: Mercury, Venus, Mars, Jupiter, and Saturn. Mercury is visible infrequently, and only just after sunset or just before sunrise because it is so close to the Sun. Venus often shines brightly in the early evening in the west or before dawn in the east. If you see a very bright "star" in the early evening or early morning, it is probably Venus. Jupiter, when it is visible at night, is the brightest object in the sky besides the Moon and Venus. Mars is often recognizable by its reddish color, though you should check a star chart to make sure you aren't looking at a bright red star. Saturn is also easy to see with the naked eye, but because many stars are just as bright as Saturn, it helps to know where to look. (It also helps to know that planets tend not to twinkle as much as stars.) Sometimes several planets may appear close together in the sky, offering a particularly beautiful sight (Figure 2.31).

Why was planetary motion so hard to explain?

Over the course of a single night, planets behave like all other objects in the sky—Earth's rotation makes them appear to rise in the east and set in the west. But if you continue to watch the planets night after night, you will notice that their movements among the constellations are quite complex. Instead of moving steadily eastward relative to the stars, like the Sun and Moon, the planets vary substantially in both speed and brightness.

FIGURE 2.31 This photograph shows a rare planetary grouping in which all five planets that are easily visible to the naked eye appeared close together in the sky. It was taken near Chatsworth, New Jersey, just after sunset on April 23, 2002. The next such close grouping of these five planets in our sky will not occur until September 2040.

Moreover, while the planets *usually* move eastward through the constellations, they occasionally reverse course, moving westward through the zodiac (Figure 2.32). These periods of **apparent retrograde motion** (*retrograde* means "backward") last from a few weeks to a few months, depending on the planet.

Apparent retrograde motion was very difficult to explain for ancient people who believed in an Earth-centered universe; after all, what could make planets sometimes turn around and go backward if everything moves in circles around Earth? The ancient Greeks nevertheless came up with some very clever ways to explain it (which we'll study in Chapter 3), but their explanations were complex and ultimately wrong.

In contrast, apparent retrograde motion has a simple explanation in a Sun-centered solar system. You can demonstrate it for yourself with the help of a friend (Figure 2.33a). Pick a spot in an open area to represent the Sun. You can represent Earth, walking counterclockwise around the Sun, while your friend represents a more distant planet (such as Mars or Jupiter) by walking counterclockwise around the Sun at a greater distance. Your friend should walk more

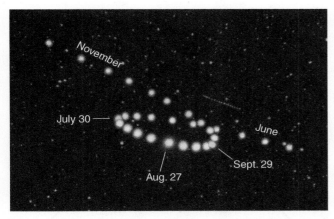

FIGURE 2.32 This composite of 29 individual photos (taken at 5- to 8-day intervals) shows Mars from June through November 2003. Notice that Mars usually moves eastward (left) relative to the stars, but reverses course during its apparent retrograde motion. Note also that Mars is biggest and brightest in the middle of the retrograde loop, because that is where it is closest to Earth in its orbit. (The white dots in a line just right of center are the planet Uranus, which by coincidence was in the same part of the sky.)

slowly than you, because more distant planets orbit the Sun more slowly. As you walk, watch how your friend appears to move relative to buildings or trees in the distance. Although both of you always walk the same way around the Sun, your friend will appear to move backward against the background during the part of your "orbit" in which you catch up to and pass him or her. To understand the apparent retrograde motions of Mercury and Venus, which are closer to the Sun than is Earth, simply switch places with your friend and repeat the demonstration.

This demonstration applies directly to the planets. For example, because Mars takes about 2 years to orbit the Sun (actually 1.88 years), it covers about half its orbit during the 1 year in which Earth makes a complete orbit. If you trace lines of sight from Earth to Mars from different points in their orbits, you will see that the line of sight usually moves eastward relative to the stars but moves westward during the time when Earth is passing Mars in its orbit (Figure 2.33b). Like your friend in the demonstration, Mars never actually changes direction. It only *appears* to change direction from our perspective on Earth.

Why did the ancient Greeks reject the real explanation for planetary motion?

If the apparent retrograde motion of the planets is so readily explained by recognizing that Earth orbits the Sun, why wasn't this idea accepted in ancient times? In fact, the idea that Earth goes around the Sun was suggested as early as 260 B.C. by the Greek astronomer Aristarchus. No one knows why Aristarchus proposed a Sun-centered solar system, but the fact that it explains planetary motion so naturally probably played a role (see Special Topic, p. 50). Nevertheless, Aristarchus's contemporaries rejected his idea, and the Sun-centered solar system did not gain wide acceptance until almost 2000 years later.

Although there were many reasons why the Greeks were reluctant to abandon the idea of an Earth-centered universe, one of the most important was their inability to detect something called **stellar parallax**. Extend your arm and hold up one finger. If you keep your finger still and alternately close your left eye and right eye, your finger will appear to jump

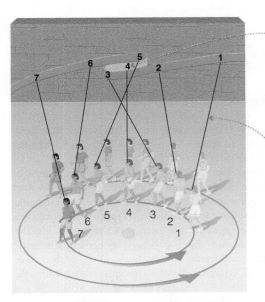

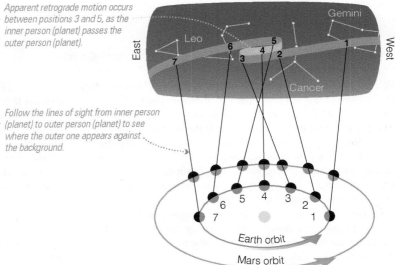

Apparent retrograde motion occurs between positions 3 and 5, as the inner person (planet) passes the outer person (planet).

Follow the lines of sight from inner person (planet) to outer person (planet) to see where the outer one appears against the background.

a The retrograde motion demonstration: Watch how your friend (in red) usually appears to move forward against the background of the building in the distance but appears to move backward as you (in blue) catch up to and pass her in your "orbit."

b This diagram shows how the same idea applies to a planet. Follow the lines of sight from Earth to Mars in numerical order. Notice that Mars appears to move westward relative to the distant stars as Earth passes it by in its orbit (roughly from points 3 to 5).

FIGURE 2.33 Interactive Figure Apparent retrograde motion—the occasional "backward" motion of the planets relative to the stars—has a simple explanation in a Sun-centered solar system.

back and forth against the background. This apparent shifting, called *parallax*, occurs because your two eyes view your finger from opposite sides of your nose. If you move your finger closer to your face, the parallax increases. If you look at a distant tree or flagpole instead of your finger, you may not notice any parallax at all. This little experiment shows that parallax depends on distance, with nearer objects exhibiting greater parallax than more distant objects.

If you now imagine that your two eyes represent Earth at opposite sides of its orbit around the Sun, and that your finger represents a relatively nearby star, you have the idea of stellar parallax. That is, because we view the stars from different places in our orbit at different times of year, nearby stars should *appear* to shift back and forth against the background of more distant stars (Figure 2.34).

Because the Greeks believed that all stars lie on the same celestial sphere, they expected to see stellar parallax in a slightly different way. If Earth orbited the Sun, they reasoned, at different times of year we would be closer to different parts of the celestial sphere and would notice changes in the angular separations of stars. However, no matter how hard they searched, they could find no sign of stellar parallax. They concluded that one of the following must be true:

1. Earth orbits the Sun, but the stars are so far away that stellar parallax is undetectable to the naked eye.

2. There is no stellar parallax because Earth remains stationary at the center of the universe.

Aside from a few notable exceptions such as Aristarchus, the Greeks rejected the correct answer (the first one) because they could not imagine that the stars could be *that* far away. Today, we can detect stellar parallax with the aid of telescopes, providing direct proof that Earth really does orbit the Sun. Careful

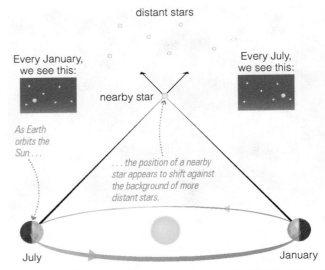

FIGURE 2.34 Stellar parallax is an apparent shift in the position of a nearby star as we look at it from different places in Earth's orbit. This figure is greatly exaggerated; in reality, the amount of shift is far too small to detect with the naked eye.

measurements of stellar parallax also provide the most reliable means of measuring distances to nearby stars [Section 15.1].

THINK ABOUT IT

How far apart are opposite sides of Earth's orbit? How far away are the nearest stars? Using the 1-to-10-billion scale from Chapter 1, describe the challenge of detecting stellar parallax.

The ancient mystery of the planets drove much of the historical debate over Earth's place in the universe. In many ways, the modern technological society we take for granted

You've probably heard of Copernicus, whose work in the middle of the 16th century started the revolution that ultimately overturned the ancient belief in an Earth-centered universe [Section 3.3]. However, Copernicus was *not* the first person to propose the idea that Earth goes around the Sun. This idea had already been suggested long before by the Greek scientist Aristarchus (c. 310–230 B.C.).

Little of Aristarchus's work survives to the present day, so we cannot know what motivated him to suggest an idea so contrary to the prevailing view of an Earth-centered universe. However, it's quite likely that he was motivated by the fact that a Sun-centered system offers a much more natural explanation for the apparent retrograde motion of the planets. To account for the lack of detectable stellar parallax, Aristarchus suggested that the stars were extremely far away.

Aristarchus further strengthened his argument by estimating the sizes of the Moon and the Sun. By observing the shadow of Earth on the Moon during a lunar eclipse, he estimated the Moon's diameter to be about one-third of Earth's diameter—only slightly more than the actual value. He then used a geometric argument, based on measuring the angle between the Moon and the Sun at first- and third-quarter phases, to conclude that the Sun must be larger than Earth.

(Aristarchus's measurements were imprecise, so he estimated the Sun's diameter to be about seven times Earth's rather than the correct value of about 100 times.) His conclusion that the Sun is larger than Earth may have been another reason why he felt that Earth should orbit the Sun, rather than vice versa.

Although Aristarchus was probably the first to suggest that Earth orbits the Sun, his ideas were in large part built upon the work of earlier scholars. For example, Heracleides (c. 388–315 B.C.) had previously suggested that Earth rotates. Aristarchus may have drawn on this idea to explain the apparent daily rotation of the stars in our sky. Heracleides also suggested that not all heavenly bodies circle Earth: Based on the fact that Mercury and Venus always stay fairly close to the Sun in the sky, he argued that these two planets must orbit the Sun. In suggesting that *all* the planets orbit the Sun, Aristarchus was extending the ideas of Heracleides and others before him.

Aristarchus gained little support among his contemporaries, but his ideas never died, and Copernicus was aware of them when he proposed his own version of the Sun-centered system. Thus, our modern understanding of the universe owes at least some debt to the remarkable vision of a man who lived more than 2200 years ago.

today can be traced directly to the scientific revolution that began in the quest to explain the strange wanderings of the planets among the stars in our sky. We will turn our attention to this revolution in the next chapter.

THE BIG PICTURE

• Putting Chapter 2 into Context

In this chapter, we surveyed the phenomena of our sky. Keep the following "big picture" ideas in mind as you continue your study of astronomy:

■ You can enhance your enjoyment of astronomy by observing the sky. The more you learn about the appearance and apparent motions of the sky, the more you will appreciate what you can see in the universe.

■ From our vantage point on Earth, it is convenient to imagine that we are at the center of a great celestial sphere—even though we really are on a planet orbiting a star in a vast universe. We can then understand what we see in the local sky by thinking about how the celestial sphere appears from our latitude.

■ Most of the phenomena of the sky are relatively easy to observe and understand. The more complex phenomena—particularly eclipses and apparent retrograde motion of the planets—challenged our ancestors for thousands of years. The desire to understand these phenomena helped drive the development of science and technology.

SUMMARY OF KEY CONCEPTS

2.1 PATTERNS IN THE NIGHT SKY

■ **What does the universe look like from Earth?** Stars and other celestial objects appear to lie on a great  **celestial sphere** surrounding Earth. We divide the celestial sphere into **constellations** with well-defined borders. From any location on Earth, we see half the celestial sphere at any one time as the dome of our **local sky,** in which the **horizon** is the boundary between Earth and sky, the **zenith** is the point directly overhead, and the **meridian** runs from due south to due north through the zenith.

■ **Why do stars rise and set?**  Earth's rotation makes stars appear to circle around Earth each day. A star whose complete circle lies above our horizon is said to be **circumpolar.** Other stars have circles that cross the horizon, making them rise in the east and set in the west each day.

■ **Why do the constellations we see depend on latitude and time of year?** The visible constellations vary with time of year because our night sky lies in different directions in space as we orbit the Sun. The constellations vary with **latitude** because your latitude determines the orientation of your horizon relative to the celestial sphere. The sky does not vary with **longitude.**

2.2 THE REASON FOR SEASONS

■ **What causes the seasons?** The tilt of Earth's axis causes the seasons. The axis points in the same direction  throughout the year, so as Earth orbits the Sun, sunlight hits different parts of Earth more directly at different times of year.

■ **How does the orientation of Earth's axis change**  **with time?** Earth's 26,000-year cycle of **precession** changes the orientation of the axis in space, although the tilt remains about $23\frac{1}{2}°$. The changing orientation of the axis does not affect the pattern of seasons, but it changes the identity of the north star and shifts the locations of the solstices and equinoxes in Earth's orbit.

2.3 THE MOON, OUR CONSTANT COMPANION

■ **Why do we see phases of the Moon?** The **phase** of the Moon depends on its position relative to the Sun as it orbits Earth. The half of the Moon facing the Sun is always illuminated while the other half is dark, but from Earth we see varying combinations of the illuminated and dark faces.

■ **What causes eclipses?** We see a **lunar eclipse**  when Earth's shadow falls on the Moon and a **solar eclipse** when the Moon blocks our view of the Sun. We do not see an eclipse at every new and full moon because the Moon's orbit is slightly inclined to the ecliptic plane. Eclipses come in different types, depending on where the dark **umbral** and lighter **penumbral** shadows fall.

2.4 THE ANCIENT MYSTERY OF THE PLANETS

■ **Why was planetary motion so hard to explain?**

Planets generally move eastward relative to the stars over the course of the year, but for weeks or months they reverse course during periods of **apparent retrograde motion.** This motion occurs when Earth passes by (or is passed by) another planet in its orbit, but it posed a major mystery to ancient people who assumed Earth to be at the center of the universe.

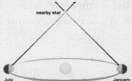

■ **Why did the ancient Greeks reject the real explanation for planetary motion?** The Greeks rejected the idea that Earth goes around the Sun in part because they could not detect **stellar parallax**—slight apparent shifts in stellar positions over the course of the year. To most Greeks, it seemed unlikely that the stars could be so far away as to make parallax undetectable to the naked eye, even though that is, in fact, the case.

EXERCISES AND PROBLEMS

For instructor-assigned homework go to www.masteringastronomy.com.

REVIEW QUESTIONS

Short-Answer Questions Based on the Reading

1. What are *constellations?* How did they get their names?
2. Suppose you were making a model of the celestial sphere with a ball. Briefly describe all the things you would need to mark on your celestial sphere.
3. On a clear, dark night, the sky may appear to be "full" of stars. Does this appearance accurately reflect the way stars are distributed in space? Explain.
4. Why does the *local sky* look like a dome? Define *horizon, zenith,* and *meridian.* How do we describe the location of an object in the local sky?
5. Explain why we can measure only *angular sizes* and *angular distances* for objects in the sky. What are *arcminutes* and *arcseconds?*
6. What are *circumpolar stars?* Are more stars circumpolar at the North Pole or in the United States? Explain.
7. What are *latitude* and *longitude?* Does the sky vary with latitude? Does it vary with longitude? Explain.
8. What is the *zodiac,* and why do we see different parts of it at different times of year?
9. Suppose Earth's axis had no tilt. Would we still have seasons? Why or why not?
10. Briefly describe what is special about the summer and winter solstices and the spring and fall equinoxes.
11. What is *precession,* and how does it affect the sky that we see from Earth?
12. Briefly describe the Moon's cycle of *phases.* Can you ever see a full moon at noon? Explain.
13. What do we mean when we say that the Moon exhibits *synchronous rotation?* What does this tell us about the Moon's periods of rotation and orbit?
14. Why don't we see an *eclipse* at every new and full moon? Describe the conditions needed for a *solar* or *lunar eclipse.*
15. What do we mean by the *apparent retrograde motion* of the planets? Why was it difficult for ancient astronomers to explain? How do we explain it today?
16. What is *stellar parallax?* How did an inability to detect it support the ancient belief in an Earth-centered universe?

TEST YOUR UNDERSTANDING

Does It Make Sense?

Decide whether the statement makes sense (or is clearly true) or does not make sense (or is clearly false). Explain clearly; not all of these have definitive answers, so your explanation is more important than your chosen answer.

17. The constellation Orion didn't exist when my grandfather was a child.
18. When I looked into the dark lanes of the Milky Way with my binoculars, I saw what must have been a cluster of distant galaxies.
19. Last night the Moon was so big that it stretched for a mile across the sky.
20. I live in the United States, and during my first trip to Argentina I saw many constellations that I'd never seen before.
21. Last night I saw Jupiter right in the middle of the Big Dipper. (*Hint:* Is the Big Dipper part of the zodiac?)
22. Last night I saw Mars move westward through the sky in its apparent retrograde motion.
23. Although all the known stars appear to rise in the east and set in the west, we might someday discover a star that will appear to rise in the west and set in the east.
24. If Earth's orbit were a perfect circle, we would not have seasons.
25. Because of precession, someday it will be summer everywhere on Earth at the same time.
26. This morning I saw the full moon setting at about the same time the Sun was rising.

Quick Quiz

Choose the best answer to each of the following. Explain your reasoning with one or more complete sentences.

27. Two stars that are in the same constellation (a) must both be part of the same cluster of stars in space. (b) must both have been discovered at about the same time. (c) may actually be very far away from each other.
28. The north celestial pole is 35° above your northern horizon. This tells you that (a) you are at latitude 35°N. (b) you are at longitude 35°E. (c) you are at latitude 35°S.

29. Beijing and Philadelphia have about the same latitude but very different longitudes. Therefore, tonight's night sky in these two places (a) will look about the same. (b) will have completely different sets of constellations. (c) will have partially different sets of constellations.

30. In winter, Earth's axis points toward the star Polaris. In spring, (a) the axis also points toward Polaris. (b) the axis points toward Vega. (c) the axis points toward the Sun.

31. When it is summer in Australia, in the United States it is (a) winter. (b) summer. (c) spring.

32. If the Sun rises precisely due east, (a) you must be located at Earth's equator. (b) it must be the day of either the spring or the fall equinox. (c) it must be the day of the summer solstice.

33. A week after full moon, the Moon's phase is (a) first quarter. (b) third quarter. (c) new.

34. The fact that we always see the same face of the Moon tells us that (a) the Moon does not rotate. (b) the Moon's rotation period is the same as its orbital period. (c) the Moon looks the same on both sides.

35. If there is going to be a total lunar eclipse tonight, then you know that (a) the Moon's phase is full. (b) the Moon's phase is new. (c) the Moon is unusually close to Earth.

36. When we see Saturn going through a period of apparent retrograde motion, it means (a) Saturn is temporarily moving backward in its orbit of the Sun. (b) Earth is passing Saturn in its orbit, with both planets on the same side of the Sun. (c) Saturn and Earth must be on opposite sides of the Sun.

PROCESS OF SCIENCE

Examining How Science Works

37. *Earth-Centered or Sun-Centered?* The phenomena discussed in this chapter are all visible to the naked eye and therefore have been known throughout human history, even during the thousands of years when Earth was assumed to be at the center of the universe. For each of the following, decide whether the phenomenon is consistent or inconsistent with a belief in an Earth-centered system. If consistent, describe how. If inconsistent, explain why, and also explain why the inconsistency did not immediately lead people to abandon the Earth-centered model.
a. The daily paths of stars through the sky b. Seasons c. Phases of the Moon d. Eclipses e. Apparent retrograde motion of the planets

38. *Shadow Phases.* Many people incorrectly guess that the phases of the Moon are caused by Earth's shadow falling on the Moon. How would you go about convincing a friend that the phases of the Moon have nothing to do with Earth's shadow? Describe the observations you would use to show that Earth's shadow can't be the cause of phases.

INVESTIGATE FURTHER

In-Depth Questions to Increase Your Understanding

Short-Answer/Essay Questions

39. *New Planet.* A planet in another solar system has a circular orbit and an axis tilt of 35°. Would you expect this planet to have seasons? If so, would you expect them to be more extreme than the seasons on Earth? If not, why not?

40. *Your View of the Sky*
a. Find your latitude and longitude, and state the source of your information. b. Describe the altitude and direction in your sky at which the north or south celestial pole appears. c. Is Polaris a circumpolar star in your sky? Explain.

41. *View from the Moon.* Assume you live on the Moon near the center of the face that looks toward Earth.
a. Suppose you see a full earth in your sky. What phase of the Moon would people on Earth see? Explain. b. Suppose people on Earth see a full moon. What phase would you see for Earth? Explain. c. Suppose people on Earth see a waxing gibbous moon. What phase would you see for Earth? Explain. d. Suppose people on Earth are viewing a total lunar eclipse. What would you see from your home on the Moon? Explain.

42. *View from the Sun.* Suppose you lived on the Sun (and could ignore the heat). Would you still see the Moon go through phases as it orbits Earth? Why or why not?

43. *A Farther Moon.* Suppose the distance to the Moon were twice its actual value. Would it still be possible to have a total solar eclipse? Why or why not?

44. *A Smaller Earth.* Suppose Earth were smaller. Would solar eclipses be any different? If so, how? What about lunar eclipses?

45. *Observing Planetary Motion.* Find out which planets are currently visible in your evening sky. At least once a week, observe the planets and draw a diagram showing the position of each visible planet relative to stars in a zodiac constellation. From week to week, note how the planets are moving relative to the stars. Can you see any of the apparently wandering features of planetary motion? Explain.

46. *A Connecticut Yankee.* Find the book *A Connecticut Yankee in King Arthur's Court* by Mark Twain. Read the portion that deals with the Connecticut Yankee's prediction of an eclipse. In a one-to two-page essay, summarize the episode and explain how it helped the Connecticut Yankee gain power.

Quantitative Problems

Be sure to show all calculations clearly and state your final answers in complete sentences.

47. *Arcminutes and Arcseconds.* There are 360° in a full circle.
a. How many arcminutes are in a full circle? b. How many arcseconds are in a full circle? c. The Moon's angular size is about $\frac{1}{2}$°. What is this in arcminutes? In arcseconds?

48. *Latitude Distance.* Earth's radius is approximately 6370 km.
a. What is Earth's circumference? b. What distance is represented by each degree of latitude? c. What distance is represented by each arcminute of latitude? d. Can you give similar answers for the distances represented by a degree or arcminute of longitude? Why or why not?

49. *Angular Conversions I.* The following angles are given in degrees and fractions of degrees. Rewrite them in degrees, arcminutes, and arcseconds.
a. 24.3° b. 1.59° c. 0.1° d. 0.01° e. 0.001°

50. *Angular Conversions II.* The following angles are given in degrees, arcminutes, and arcseconds. Rewrite them in degrees and fractions of degrees.
a. 7°38'42" b. 12'54" c. 1°59'59" d. 1' e. 1"

51. *Moon Speed.* The Moon takes about $27\frac{1}{3}$ days to complete each orbit of Earth. About how fast is the Moon going as it orbits Earth? Give your answer in km/hr.

52. *Scale of the Moon.* The Moon's diameter is about 3500 km and its average distance from Earth is about 380,000 km. How big and how far from Earth is the Moon on the 1-to-10-billion scale used in Chapter 1? Compare the size of the Moon's orbit to the size of the Sun on this scale.

53. *Angular Size of Your Finger.* Measure the width of your index finger and the length of your arm. Based on your measurements, calculate the angular width of your index finger at arm's length. Does your result agree with the approximations shown in Figure 2.7c? Explain.

54. *Find the Sun's Diameter.* The Sun has an angular diameter of about 0.5° and an average distance of about 150 million km. What is the Sun's approximate physical diameter? Compare your answer to the actual value of 1,390,000 km.

55. *Find a Star's Diameter.* The supergiant star Betelgeuse has a measured angular diameter of 0.044 arcsecond. Its distance has been measured to be 427 light-years. What is the actual diameter of Betelgeuse? Compare your answer to the size of our Sun and the Earth-Sun distance.

56. *Eclipse Conditions.* The Moon's precise equatorial diameter is 3476 km, and its orbital distance from Earth varies between 356,400 km and 406,700 km. The Sun's diameter is 1,390,000 km, and its distance from Earth ranges between 147.5 and 152.6 million km.
a. Find the Moon's angular size at its minimum and maximum distances from Earth. b. Find the Sun's angular size at its minimum and maximum distances from Earth. c. Based on your answers to (a) and (b), is it possible to have a total solar eclipse when the Moon and Sun are both at their maximum distances? Explain.

Discussion Questions

57. *Earth-Centered Language.* Many common phrases reflect the ancient Earth-centered view of our universe. For example, the phrase "the Sun rises each day" implies that the Sun is really moving over Earth. We know that the Sun only *appears* to rise as the rotation of Earth carries us to a place where we can see the Sun in our sky. Identify other common phrases that imply an Earth-centered viewpoint.

58. *Flat Earth Society.* Believe it or not, there is an organization called the Flat Earth Society. Its members hold that Earth is flat and that all indications to the contrary (such as pictures of Earth from space) are fabrications made as part of a conspiracy to hide the truth from the public. Discuss the evidence for a round Earth and how you can check it for yourself. In light of the evidence, is it possible that the Flat Earth Society is correct? Defend your opinion.

Web Projects

59. *Sky Information.* Search the Web for sources of daily information about sky phenomena (such as lunar phases, times of sunrise and sunset, or dates of equinoxes and solstices). Identify and briefly describe your favorite source.

60. *Constellations.* Search the Web for information about the constellations and their mythology. Write a short report about one or more constellations.

61. *Upcoming Eclipse.* Find information about an upcoming solar or lunar eclipse. Write a short report about how you could best observe the eclipse, including any necessary travel to a viewing site, and what you could expect to see. Bonus: Describe how you could photograph the eclipse.

VISUAL SKILLS CHECK

Use the following questions to check your understanding of some of the many types of visual information used in astronomy. Answers are provided in Appendix J. For additional practice, try the Chapter 2 Visual Quiz at www.masteringastronomy.com.

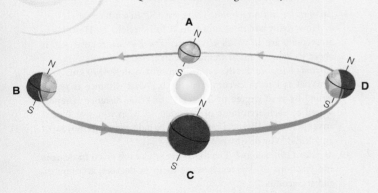

The figure above is a typical diagram used to describe Earth's seasons.

1. Which of the four labeled points (A through D) represents the beginning of summer for the Northern Hemisphere?
2. Which of the four labeled points represents the beginning of summer for the Southern Hemisphere?
3. Which of the four labeled points represents the beginning of spring for the Northern Hemisphere?
4. Which of the four labeled points represents the beginning of spring for the Southern Hemisphere?
5. Diagrams like the one in the figure are useful for representing seasons, but they can also be misleading because they exaggerate the sizes of Earth and the Sun relative to the orbit. If Earth were correctly scaled relative to the orbit in the figure, how big would it be?
a. about half the size shown b. about 2 millimeters across
c. about 0.1 millimeter across d. microscopic

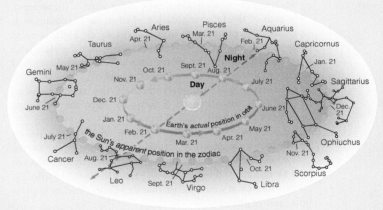

The figure above (based on Figure 2.12) shows the Sun's path through the constellations of the zodiac.

6. As viewed from Earth, in which zodiac constellation does the Sun appear to be located on April 21?
a. Leo b. Aquarius c. Libra d. Aries
7. If the date is April 21, what zodiac constellation will be visible on your meridian at midnight?
a. Leo b. Aquarius c. Libra d. Aries
8. If the date is April 21, what zodiac constellation will you see setting in the west shortly after sunset?
a. Scorpius b. Pisces c. Taurus d. Virgo

3

THE SCIENCE OF ASTRONOMY

We especially need imagination in science. It is not all mathematics, nor all logic, but is somewhat beauty and poetry.

—Maria Mitchell (1818–1889), astronomer and the first woman elected to the American Academy of Arts and Sciences

Today we know that Earth is a planet orbiting a rather ordinary star, in a galaxy of more than a hundred billion stars, in an incredibly vast universe. We know that Earth, along with the entire cosmos, is in constant motion. We know that, on the scale of cosmic time, human civilization has existed for only the briefest moment. How did we manage to learn these things?

It wasn't easy. Astronomy is the oldest of the sciences, with roots extending as far back as recorded history allows us to see. But the most impressive advances in knowledge have come in just the past few centuries.

In this chapter, we will trace how modern astronomy grew from its roots in ancient observations, including those of the Greeks. We'll pay special attention to the unfolding of the Copernican revolution, which overturned the ancient belief in an Earth-centered universe and laid the foundation for the rise of our technological civilization. Finally, we'll explore the nature of modern science and how science can be distinguished from nonscience.

3.1 THE ANCIENT ROOTS OF SCIENCE

A common stereotype holds that scientists walk around in white lab coats and somehow think differently than other people. In reality, scientific thinking is a fundamental part of human nature. In this section, we will trace the roots of science to experiences common to nearly all people and nearly all cultures.

In what ways do all humans use scientific thinking?

Scientific thinking comes naturally to us. By about a year of age, a baby notices that objects fall to the ground when she drops them. She lets go of a ball—it falls. She pushes a plate of food from her high chair—it falls, too. She continues to drop all kinds of objects, and they all plummet to Earth. Through her powers of observation, the baby learns about the physical world, finding that things fall when they are unsupported. Eventually, she becomes so certain of this fact that, to her parents' delight, she no longer needs to test it continually.

One day somebody gives the baby a helium balloon. She releases it, and to her surprise it rises to the ceiling! Her understanding of nature must be revised. She now knows that the principle "all things fall" does not represent the whole truth, although it still serves her quite well in most situations. It will be years before she learns enough about the atmosphere, the force of gravity, and the concept of density to understand *why* the balloon rises when most

other objects fall. For now, she is delighted to observe something new and unexpected.

The baby's experience with falling objects and balloons exemplifies scientific thinking. In essence, science is a way of learning about nature through careful observation and trial-and-error experiments. Rather than thinking differently than other people, modern scientists simply are trained to organize everyday thinking in a way that makes it easier for them to share their discoveries and use their collective wisdom.

THINK ABOUT IT

Describe a few cases where you have learned by trial and error while cooking, participating in sports, fixing something, or working at a job.

Just as learning to communicate through language, art, or music is a gradual process for a child, the development of science has been a gradual process for humanity. Science in its modern form requires painstaking attention to detail, relentless testing of each piece of information to ensure its reliability, and a willingness to give up old beliefs that are not consistent with observed facts about the physical world. For professional scientists, these demands are the "hard work" part of the job. At heart, professional scientists are like the baby with the balloon, delighted by the unexpected and motivated by those rare moments when they—and all of us—learn something new about the universe.

How did astronomical observations benefit ancient societies?

We will discuss modern science shortly, but first we will explore how it arose from the observations of ancient peoples. Our exploration begins in central Africa, where people long ago learned to predict the weather with reasonable accuracy by making careful observations of the Moon. Remember that the Moon begins its monthly cycle as a crescent in the western sky just after sunset. Through long traditions of sky watching, central African societies discovered that the orientation of the crescent "horns" relative to the horizon is closely tied to local rainfall patterns (Figure 3.1). The technique works because the orientation depends on the relative positions of the Sun and Moon along the ecliptic, which varies with the time of year, and because the equatorial climate features a rainy season and a dry season rather than the four seasons we experience at temperate latitudes.

Why did ancient people make such careful and detailed observations of the sky? In part, it was probably to satisfy their inherent curiosity. But astronomy also played a practical role in their lives. They used the changing positions of the Sun, Moon, and stars to keep track of the time and seasons, crucial skills for people who depended on agriculture. This ability may seem quaint today, when digital watches tell us the precise time and date, but it required considerable knowledge and skill in ancient times, when the only clocks and calendars were in the sky.

Modern measures of time come directly from ancient observations of motion in the sky. The length of our day is the time it takes the Sun to make one full circuit of the sky.

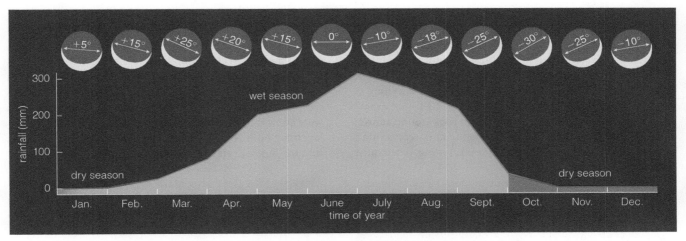

FIGURE 3.1 Science is rooted in careful observation of the world around us. This diagram shows how central Africans used the orientation of the waxing crescent moon to predict rainfall. The graph depicts the annual rainfall pattern in central Nigeria, and the Moon diagrams show the varying angle of the "horns" of a waxing crescent moon relative to the western horizon. (Adapted from *Ancient Astronomers* by Anthony F. Aveni.)

The length of a month comes from the Moon's cycle of phases [Section 2.3], and our year is based on the cycle of the seasons [Section 2.2]. The 7 days of the week were named after the seven naked-eye objects that appear to move among the constellations: the Sun, the Moon, and the five planets* recognized in ancient times (Table 3.1).

What did ancient civilizations achieve in astronomy?

Nearly all ancient civilizations practiced astronomy at some level. Many built remarkable structures for observing the sky. Let's explore a few of the ways that ancient societies studied the sky.

---

*The word *planet*, which means "wanderer," originally referred to the Sun and the Moon as well as the five visible planets. Earth was not considered a planet in ancient times, since it was assumed to be stationary at the center of the universe.

TABLE 3.1 The Seven Days of the Week and the Astronomical Objects They Honor

The seven days were originally linked directly to the seven objects. The correspondence is no longer perfect, but the overall pattern is clear in many languages; some English names come from Germanic gods.

Object	Germanic God	English	French	Spanish
Sun	—	Sunday	dimanche	domingo
Moon	—	Monday	lundi	lunes
Mars	Tiw	Tuesday	mardi	martes
Mercury	Woden	Wednesday	mercredi	miércoles
Jupiter	Thor	Thursday	jeudi	jueves
Venus	Fria	Friday	vendredi	viernes
Saturn	—	Saturday	samedi	sábado

Determining the Time of Day In the daytime, ancient peoples could tell time by observing the Sun's path through the sky. Many cultures probably used the shadows cast by sticks as simple sundials [Section S1.2]. The ancient Egyptians built huge obelisks, often decorated in homage to the Sun, that probably also served as simple clocks (Figure 3.2).

FIGURE 3.2 This ancient Egyptian obelisk, which stands 83 feet tall and weighs 331 tons, resides in St. Peter's Square at the Vatican in Rome. It is one of 21 surviving obelisks from ancient Egypt, most of which are now scattered around the world. Shadows cast by the obelisks may have been used to tell time.

At night, ancient people could estimate the time from the position and phase of the Moon by using the ideas we discussed in Chapter 2 (see Figure 2.22). For example, a first-quarter moon sets around midnight, so it is not yet midnight if the first-quarter moon is still above your western horizon. The positions of the stars can also indicate the time, as long as you know the approximate date (see Figure 2.14). For example, in December the constellation Orion rises around sunset, reaches the meridian around midnight, and sets around sunrise. Hence, if it is winter and Orion is setting, dawn must be approaching.

We can trace the origins of our modern clock to ancient Egypt, some 4000 years ago. The Egyptians divided the daylight into 12 equal parts, and we still break the 24-hour day into 12 hours each of a.m. and p.m. (The abbreviations a.m. and p.m. stand for the Latin terms *ante meridiem* and *post meridiem*, respectively, which mean "before the middle of the day" and "after the middle of the day.") However, unlike our modern hours, the Egyptian "hours" varied in length because the amount of daylight varies during the year. For example, the daylight "summer hours" were longer than the daylight "winter hours," because one-twelfth of the daylight lasts longer in summer than in winter. Only much later in history did the hour become a fixed amount of time, subdivided into 60 equal minutes each consisting of 60 equal seconds.

The Egyptians also divided the night into 12 equal parts. Egyptian *star clocks*, often found painted on the coffin lids of Egyptian pharaohs, cataloged where particular stars appeared in the sky at particular times of night and particular times of year. By knowing the date from their calendar and observing the positions of particular stars in the sky, the Egyptians could use the star clocks to estimate the time of night.

By about 1500 B.C., Egyptians had abandoned star clocks in favor of clocks that measure time by the flow of water through an opening of a particular size, just as hourglasses measure time by the flow of sand through a narrow neck.* These *water clocks* had the advantage of working even when the sky was cloudy. They eventually became the primary timekeeping instruments for many cultures, including the Greeks, Romans, and Chinese. Water clocks, in turn, were replaced by mechanical clocks in the 17th century and by electronic clocks in the 20th century. Despite the availability of other types of clocks, sundials were common throughout ancient times and remain popular today both for their decorative value and as reminders that the Sun and stars once were our only guides to time.

Marking the Seasons Many ancient cultures built structures to help them mark the seasons. One of the oldest standing human-made structures served such a purpose: Stonehenge (Figure 3.3). Stonehenge was both an astronomical device for keeping track of the seasons and a social and religious gathering place.

Among the most spectacular structures used to mark the seasons was the Templo Mayor in the Aztec city of Tenochtitlán, located in modern-day Mexico City (Figure 3.4). Twin temples stood on a flat-topped, 150-foot-high pyramid. From the vantage point of a royal observer watching from the opposite side of the plaza, the Sun rose through the notch between the temples on the equinoxes. Before the Conquistadors destroyed it, Spanish visitors reported elaborate rituals at the Templo Mayor, sometimes including human sacrifice, at times determined by astronomical observations. After its destruction, stones from the Templo Mayor were used to build a cathedral in the great plaza of Mexico City.

Many cultures aligned their buildings and streets with the cardinal directions (north, south, east, and west), in some cases so that their cities would represent miniature versions of the heavens. This type of alignment is found at such diverse sites as the Egyptian pyramids and the Forbidden City in China and

---

*Hourglasses using sand were not invented until about the 8th century A.D., long after the advent of water clocks. Natural sand grains vary in size, so making accurate hourglasses required technology for making uniform grains of sand.

a The remains of Stonehenge today.

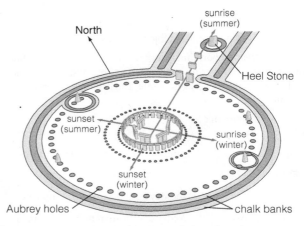

b This sketch shows how archaeologists believe Stonehenge looked upon its completion in about 1550 B.C. Several astronomical alignments are shown as they appear from the center. For example, the Sun rises directly over the Heel Stone on the summer solstice.

FIGURE 3.3 Stonehenge, in southern England, was built in stages from about 2750 B.C. to about 1550 B.C.

FIGURE 3.4 This scale model shows the Templo Mayor and the surrounding plaza as they are thought to have looked before the Spanish Conquistadors destroyed them. The structure was used to help mark the seasons.

FIGURE 3.5 This large structure, more than 20 meters in diameter, is an Anasazi kiva in Chaco Canyon, New Mexico. It was built approximately 1000 years ago. Its main axis is aligned almost precisely north-south.

among ceremonial kivas built by the Anasazi of the American southwest (Figure 3.5). Many modern cities retain this layout, which is why you'll find so many streets that run directly north-south or east-west.

Other structures were used to mark the Sun's position on special dates such as the winter or summer solstice. For example, the ancient Anasazi carved a 19-turn spiral—the *Sun Dagger*—on a vertical cliff face in Chaco Canyon, New Mexico (Figure 3.6). Three large slabs of rock in front of the spiral produce different patterns of light and shadow throughout the year. The slabs form a dagger of sunlight that pierces the center of the carved spiral only once each year—at noon on the summer solstice—while two daggers of light bracket the spiral at winter solstice, and a single dagger cuts through the center of a smaller spiral on each equinox. The Sun Dagger can even be used to observe an 18.6-year cycle of the moon.

Lunar Calendars Ancient civilizations also tracked the lunar phases, and some used the lunar cycle (from one new moon to the next) as the basis for their calendar. A basic lunar calendar has 12 months, with some months lasting 29 days

and others lasting 30 days; the lengths are chosen to make the average agree with the approximately $29\frac{1}{2}$-day lunar cycle. A 12-month lunar calendar therefore has only 354 or 355 days, or about 11 days fewer than a calendar based on the Sun. Such a calendar is still used in the Muslim religion. That is why the month-long fast of Ramadan (the ninth month) begins about 11 days earlier with each subsequent year.

Some cultures that used lunar calendars apparently did not like the idea of having their months cycle through the seasons over time, so they modified their calendars to take advantage of the fact that the lunar phases repeat on the same solar dates about every 19 years. For example, there was a full moon on February 28, 2010, and there will be a full moon 19 years later, on February 28, 2029. This 19-year cycle on which the dates of lunar phases repeat is called the *Metonic cycle,* because the Greek astronomer Meton recognized it in 432 B.C. (However, Babylonian astronomers almost certainly knew of the cycle centuries earlier.)

Lunar phases repeat with the Metonic cycle because 19 solar years is almost precisely 235 lunar months (see Problem 47 at the end of this chapter). A lunar calendar will therefore remain

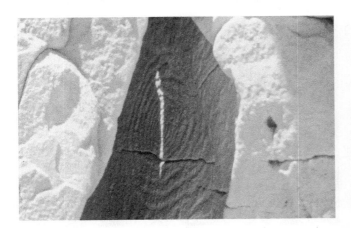

a A single dagger of sunlight pierces the center of the carved spiral only at noon on the summer solstice.

b Fajada butte in Chaco Canyon, New Mexico, where the Sun Dagger is located on a vertical cliff near the top.

FIGURE 3.6 The Sun Dagger. Three large slabs of rock in front of the carved spiral produce patterns of light and shadow that vary throughout the year.

roughly in sync with a solar calendar if it has 235 months in each 19-year period. Because 19 years with 12 months each would mean only 19 × 12 = 228 months, or 7 short of the needed 235 months, lunar calendars that follow the Metonic cycle add a thirteenth month to 7 of every 19 years. For example, the Jewish calendar has a thirteenth month in the third, sixth, eighth, eleventh, fourteenth, seventeenth, and nineteenth years of each 19-year cycle. This scheme keeps the dates of Jewish holidays within about a 1-month range on a solar calendar, with precise dates repeating every 19 years. It also explains why the date of Easter changes from year to year: The New Testament ties the date of Easter to the Jewish festival of Passover. In a slight modification of the original scheme, most Western Christians now celebrate Easter on the first Sunday after the first full moon after March 21. If the full moon falls on Sunday, Easter is the following Sunday. (Eastern Orthodox churches calculate the date of Easter differently, because they base the date on the Julian rather than the Gregorian calendar [Section S1.1].)

In addition to following the lunar phases, some ancient cultures discovered other lunar cycles. In the Middle East more than 2500 years ago, the Babylonians achieved remarkable success in predicting eclipses, thanks to their recognition of the approximately 18-year saros cycle [Section 2.3]. The Mayans of Central America also appear to have been experts at eclipse prediction, as the Mayan calendar featured a sacred cycle (the *sacred round*) of 260 days—almost exactly $1\frac{1}{2}$ times the 173.32 days between successive eclipse seasons. Unfortunately, we know little more about Mayan astronomical accomplishments, because the Spanish Conquistadors burned nearly all of their writings.

The Anasazi also appear to have understood lunar cycles quite well. The rise and set positions of the full moon vary in an 18.6-year cycle (because of precession of the Moon's orbit), so the full moon rises at its most southerly point along the eastern horizon only once every 18.6 years. At this time, known as a "major lunar standstill," the shadow of the full moon passes through the slabs of rock to lie tangent to the edge of the spiral in the Sun Dagger (see Figure 3.6); 9.3 years later the lunar shadow cuts through the center of the spiral. The major lunar standstill can also be observed with structures at nearby Chimney Rock and in cliff dwellings at Colorado's Mesa Verde National Park.

Ancient Structures and Archaeoastronomy Many ancient cultures also made careful observations of planets and stars. The Chinese, for example, began keeping remarkably detailed records of astronomical observations at least 5000 years ago, allowing Chinese astronomers to make many important discoveries. By the 15th century, the Chinese had built a great observatory in Beijing, which still stands today (Figure 3.7).

It's easy to establish the astronomical intentions of ancient cultures that left extensive written records, such as the Chinese and the Egyptians. In other cases, however, claims that ancient structures served astronomical purposes can be much more difficult to evaluate.

The study of ancient structures in search of astronomical connections is called *archaeoastronomy,* a word that combines

FIGURE 3.7 This photo shows a model of the celestial sphere and other instruments on the roof of the ancient astronomical observatory in Beijing. The observatory was built in the 15th century; the instruments shown here were built later and show a European influence brought by Jesuit missionaries.

archaeology and astronomy. Scientists engaged in archaeoastronomy usually start by evaluating an ancient structure to see whether it shows any particular astronomical alignments. For example, they may check to see whether an observer in a central location would see particular stars rise above specially marked stones, or whether sunlight enters through a window only on special days like the solstices or equinoxes. However, the mere existence of astronomical alignments is not enough to establish that a structure had an astronomical purpose; the alignments may be coincidental.

Native American Medicine Wheels—stone circles found throughout the northern plains of the United States—offer an example of the difficulty of trying to establish the intentions of ancient builders. In the 1970s, a study of the Big Horn Medicine Wheel in Wyoming (Figure 3.8) seemed to indicate that its 28 "spokes" were aligned with the rise and set of particular stars. However, later research showed that the original study had failed to take into account the motion of stars as they rise above the horizon and the way the atmosphere affects the visibility of stars at the latitude of Big Horn. In reality the spokes do *not* show any special alignments with bright stars.

FIGURE 3.8 The Big Horn Medicine Wheel in Wyoming. A study once claimed that its "spokes" have astronomically significant alignments, but later research showed the claim was in error—making this a good example of how science adapts as new data come to light.

Moreover, if Medicine Wheels really did serve an astronomical purpose, we'd expect all of them to have been built with consistent alignments—but that is not the case. Nevertheless, many popular books and articles still report the original claims regarding astronomical purposes for Medicine Wheels, even though there is no evidence to support these claims.

Other cases are more ambiguous. For example, ancient people in what is now Peru etched hundreds of lines and patterns in the sand of the Nazca desert. Many of the lines point to places where the Sun or bright stars rise at particular times of year, but that doesn't prove anything: With hundreds of lines, random chance ensures that many will have astronomical alignments no matter how or why they were made. The patterns, many of which are large figures of animals (Figure 3.9), have evoked even more debate. Some people think they may be representations of constellations recognized by the people who lived in the region, but we really do not know for sure.

THINK ABOUT IT

Animal figures like that in Figure 3.9 show up clearly only when seen from above. As a result, some UFO enthusiasts argue that the patterns must have been created by aliens. What do you think of this argument? Defend your opinion.

In some cases, scientists can use other clues to establish the intentions of ancient builders. For example, lodges built by the Pawnee in Kansas feature strategically placed holes for observing the passage of constellations that figure prominently in Pawnee folklore. The correspondence between the folklore and the structural features provides a strong case for deliberate intent rather than coincidence. Similarly, traditions of the Inca Empire of South America held that its rulers were descendents of the Sun and therefore demanded close watch of the movements of the Sun and stars. This fact supports the idea that astronomical alignments in Inca cities and ceremonial centers, such as the World Heritage Site of Machu Picchu (Figure 3.10), were deliberate rather than accidental.

A different type of evidence makes a convincing case for the astronomical sophistication of ancient Polynesians, who

FIGURE 3.10 The World Heritage Site of Machu Picchu has structures aligned with sunrise at the winter and summer solstices.

lived and traveled among the islands of the mid- and South Pacific. Navigation was crucial to their survival because the next island in a journey usually was too distant to be seen. Anthropological studies have shown that the most esteemed position in Polynesian culture was that of the Navigator, a person who had acquired the knowledge necessary to navigate great distances among the islands. The Navigators used a combination of detailed knowledge of astronomy and of the patterns of waves and swells around different islands (Figure 3.11). The stars provided the broad navigational sense, pointing the Navigators in the general direction of their destination. As they neared a destination, the wave and swell patterns guided them to their precise landing point. A Navigator memorized all his skills and passed them to the next generation through a well-developed training program. Unfortunately, with the advent of modern navigational technology, many of the skills of the Navigators have been lost.

From Observations to Science Before a structure such as Stonehenge or the Templo Mayor could be built, careful observations had to be made and repeated over and over to ensure their accuracy. Careful, repeatable observations also underlie modern science. At least some elements of modern science were therefore present among many ancient human cultures.

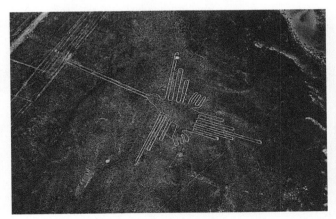

FIGURE 3.9 Hundreds of lines and patterns are etched in the sand of the Nazca desert in Peru. This aerial photo shows a large figure of a hummingbird.

FIGURE 3.11 A Micronesian stick chart, an instrument used by Polynesian Navigators to represent swell patterns around islands.

The extent to which scientific ideas developed in different societies depended on practical needs, social and political customs, and interactions with other cultures. For example, despite their "head start" in astronomical record keeping, Chinese science and technology had fallen behind that of Europe by the end of the 17th century. Some historians argue that a primary reason for this decline was that the Chinese tended to regard their science and technology as state secrets. This secrecy may have slowed Chinese scientific development by preventing the broad-based collaborative science that fueled the European advance beginning in the Renaissance.

In Central America, the ancient Mayans also were ahead of their time in many ways. For example, their system of numbers and mathematics looks distinctly modern. They invented the concept of zero some 500 years before its introduction in the Eurasian world (by Hindu mathematicians, around A.D. 600). The Aztecs, Incas, Anasazi, and other ancient peoples of the Americas may have been quite advanced in many other areas as well, but few written records survive to tell the tale.

If the circumstances of history had been different, any one of these or many other cultures might have been the first to develop what we consider to be modern science. In the end, however, history takes only one of countless possible paths. The path that led to modern science emerged from the ancient civilizations of the Mediterranean and the Middle East—especially from ancient Greece.

3.2 ANCIENT GREEK SCIENCE

By 3000 B.C., civilization was well established in two major regions of the Middle East: Egypt and Mesopotamia (Figure 3.12). Their geographical locations placed these civilizations at a crossroads for travelers, merchants, and armies from Europe, Asia, and Africa. This mixing of cultures fostered creativity and ensured that new ideas spread throughout the region.

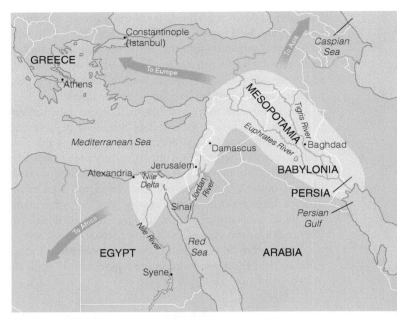

FIGURE 3.12 The highlighted region on this map shows the approximate extent of the ancient civilizations of Egypt and Mesopotamia. The map also identifies a few other places discussed in this text. The white lines show modern country borders.

Numerous great cultures arose in this region over the next 2500 years. The ancient Egyptians built the Great Pyramids (which are aligned with the cardinal directions) between 2700 and 2100 B.C., and they developed papyrus scrolls and ink-based writing, among many other inventions. The Babylonians developed arithmetic to serve in commerce and later in astronomical calculations. Indeed, many of our modern principles of commerce, law, and religion originated with the cultures of Egypt and Mesopotamia. But much of what we now call *science* came from ancient Greece, which rose as a power in the Middle East around 500 B.C.

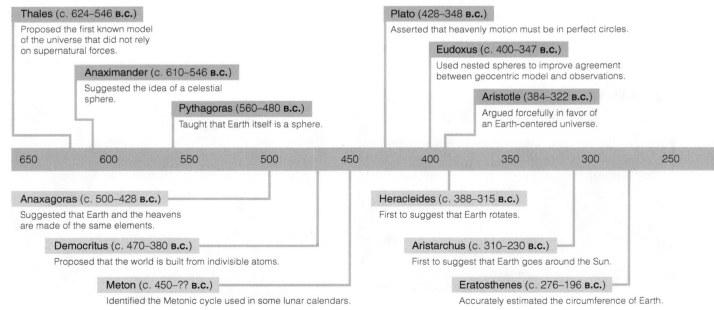

Thales (c. 624–546 **B.C.**)
Proposed the first known model of the universe that did not rely on supernatural forces.

Anaximander (c. 610–546 **B.C.**)
Suggested the idea of a celestial sphere.

Pythagoras (560–480 **B.C.**)
Taught that Earth itself is a sphere.

Plato (428–348 **B.C.**)
Asserted that heavenly motion must be in perfect circles.

Eudoxus (c. 400–347 **B.C.**)
Used nested spheres to improve agreement between geocentric model and observations.

Aristotle (384–322 **B.C.**)
Argued forcefully in favor of an Earth-centered universe.

650   600   550   500   450   400   350   300   250

Anaxagoras (c. 500–428 **B.C.**)
Suggested that Earth and the heavens are made of the same elements.

Democritus (c. 470–380 **B.C.**)
Proposed that the world is built from indivisible atoms.

Meton (c. 450–?? **B.C.**)
Identified the Metonic cycle used in some lunar calendars.

Heracleides (c. 388–315 **B.C.**)
First to suggest that Earth rotates.

Aristarchus (c. 310–230 **B.C.**)
First to suggest that Earth goes around the Sun.

Eratosthenes (c. 276–196 **B.C.**)
Accurately estimated the circumference of Earth.

FIGURE 3.13 Timeline for major Greek figures in the development of astronomy. (All these individuals are discussed in this book, but not necessarily in this chapter.)

Why does modern science trace its roots to the Greeks?

Greek philosophers developed at least three major innovations that helped pave the way for modern science. First, they developed a tradition of trying to understand nature without relying on supernatural explanations, and of working communally to debate and challenge each other's ideas. Second, the Greeks used mathematics to give precision to their ideas, which allowed them to explore the implications of new ideas in much greater depth than would have otherwise been possible. Third, while much of their philosophical activity consisted of subtle debates grounded only in thought and was not scientific in the modern sense, the Greeks also saw the power of reasoning from observations. They understood that an explanation could not be right if it disagreed with observed facts.

Perhaps the greatest Greek contribution to science came from the way they synthesized all three innovations into the idea of creating **models** of nature, a practice that is central to modern science. Scientific models differ somewhat from the models you may be familiar with in everyday life. In our daily lives, we tend to think of models as miniature physical representations, such as model cars or airplanes. In contrast, a scientific model is a conceptual representation created to explain and predict observed phenomena. For example, a model of Earth's climate uses logic and mathematics to represent what we know about how the climate works. Its purpose is to explain and predict climate changes, such as the changes that may occur with global warming. Just as a model airplane does not faithfully represent every aspect of a real airplane, a scientific model may not fully explain all our observations of nature. Nevertheless, even the failings of a scientific model can be useful, because they often point the way toward building a better model.

Greek models of nature sought to explain things such as the properties of matter and the motions of the stars, Sun, Moon, and planets. Many of the scientific ideas discussed in this book originated with the Greeks; Figure 3.13 shows a timeline of the most influential Greek figures in astronomy. Although the Greek models may seem primitive from our modern perspective, they were an enormous step forward in scientific thinking. As an example of the modeling process, let's look at how the Greeks developed models to explain celestial motion.

How did the Greeks explain planetary motion?

As we discussed in Section 2.4, most ancient Greek philosophers assumed that Earth must reside at the center of the universe. The Greeks therefore developed a sophisticated **geocentric model** of the cosmos—so named because it placed a spherical Earth at the center of the universe—that they used to explain the motions of the Sun, Moon, planets, and stars.

Early Development of the Geocentric Model We generally trace the origin of Greek science to the philosopher Thales (c. 624–546 B.C.; pronounced *thay-lees*). We encountered Thales earlier because of his legendary prediction of a solar eclipse [Section 2.3]. Thales was the first person known to have addressed the question "What is the universe made of?" without resorting to supernatural explanations. His own guess—that the universe fundamentally consists of water and that Earth is a flat disk floating in an infinite ocean—was not widely accepted even in his own time. Nevertheless, just by asking the question he suggested that the world is inherently understandable and thereby inspired others to come up with better models for the structure of the universe.

A more sophisticated idea followed soon after, proposed by a student of Thales named Anaximander (c. 610–546 B.C.). Anaximander suggested that Earth floats in empty space surrounded by a sphere of stars and two separate rings along which the Sun and Moon travel. We therefore credit him with inventing the idea of a celestial sphere [Section 2.1].

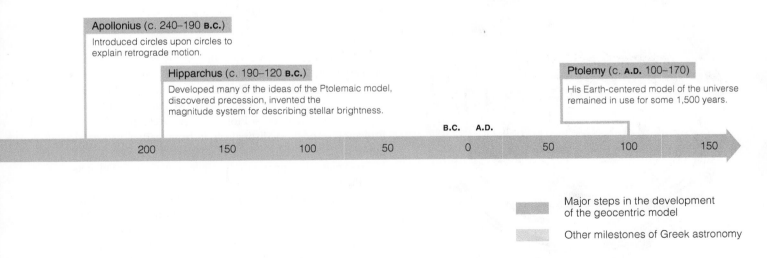

Interestingly, Anaximander imagined Earth itself to be cylindrical rather than spherical in shape. He probably chose this shape because he knew Earth had to be curved in a north-south direction to explain changes in the constellations with latitude. Because the visible constellations do not change with longitude, he saw no need for curvature in the east-west direction.

We do not know precisely when the Greeks first began to think that Earth is round, but this idea was taught as early as about 500 B.C. by the famous mathematician Pythagoras (c. 560–480 B.C.). He and his followers envisioned Earth as a sphere floating at the center of the celestial sphere. Much of their motivation for adopting a spherical Earth probably was philosophical: The Pythagoreans had a mystical interest in mathematical perfection, and they considered a sphere to be geometrically perfect. More than a century later, Aristotle cited observations of Earth's curved shadow on the Moon during lunar eclipses as evidence for a spherical Earth.

The supposed heavenly perfection of spheres influenced models of the cosmos for many centuries. Plato (428–348 B.C.), whose philosophy was based much more on pure thought than on observations, asserted that all heavenly objects move in perfect circles at constant speeds and therefore must reside on huge spheres encircling Earth (Figure 3.14). Greeks who made observations found this model problematic: The apparent retrograde motion of the planets [Section 2.4], already well known by that time, clearly showed that planets do *not* move at constant speeds around Earth.

An ingenious solution came from Plato's colleague Eudoxus (c. 400–347 B.C.), who created a model in which the Sun, the Moon, and the planets all had their own spheres nested within several other spheres. Individually, the nested spheres turned in perfect circles. By carefully choosing the sizes, rotation axes, and rotation speeds for the invisible spheres, Eudoxus was able

to make them work together in a way that reproduced many of the observed motions of the Sun, Moon, and planets in our sky. Other Greeks refined the model by comparing its predictions to observations and adding more spheres to improve the agreement.

This is how things stood when Aristotle (384–322 B.C.) arrived on the scene. Whether Eudoxus and his followers thought of the nested spheres as real physical objects is not clear, but Aristotle certainly did. In Aristotle's model, all the spheres responsible for celestial motion were transparent and interconnected like the gears of a giant machine. Earth's position at the center was explained as a natural consequence of gravity. Aristotle argued that gravity pulled heavy things toward the center of the universe (and allowed lighter things to float toward the heavens), thereby causing all the dirt, rock, and water of the universe to collect at the center and form the spherical Earth. We now know that Aristotle was wrong about both gravity and Earth's location. However, largely because of his persuasive arguments for an Earth-centered universe, the geocentric view dominated Western thought for almost 2000 years.

Ptolemy's Synthesis of the Geocentric Model Greek modeling of the cosmos culminated in the work of Claudius Ptolemy (c. A.D. 100–170; pronounced *TOL-e-mee*). Ptolemy's model still placed Earth at the center of the universe, but it differed in significant ways from the nested spheres of Eudoxus and Aristotle. We refer to Ptolemy's geocentric model as the **Ptolemaic model** to distinguish it from earlier geocentric models.

To explain the apparent retrograde motion of the planets, the Ptolemaic model applied an idea first suggested by Apollonius (c. 240–190 B.C.). This idea held that each planet moves around Earth on a small circle that turns upon a larger circle (Figure 3.15). (The small circle is sometimes called an *epicycle*, and the larger circle is called a *deferent*.) A planet following this circle-upon-circle motion traces a loop as seen from Earth, with the backward portion of the loop mimicking apparent retrograde motion.

Ptolemy also relied heavily on the work of Hipparchus (c. 190–120 B.C.), considered one of the greatest of the Greek

FIGURE 3.14 This model represents the Greek idea of the heavenly spheres (c. 400 B.C.). Earth is a sphere that rests in the center. The Moon, the Sun, and the planets all have their own spheres. The outermost sphere holds the stars.

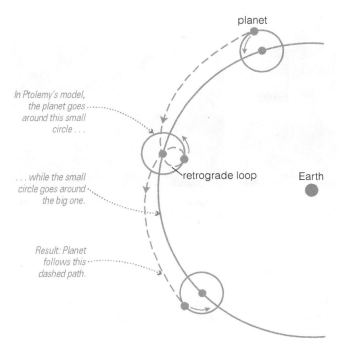

FIGURE 3.15 [Interactive Figure] This diagram shows how the Ptolemaic model accounted for apparent retrograde motion. Each planet is assumed to move around a small circle that turns upon a larger circle. The resulting path (dashed) includes a loop in which the planet goes backward as seen from Earth.

planet

In Ptolemy's model, the planet goes around this small circle . . .

. . . while the small circle goes around the big one.

retrograde loop

Earth

Result: Planet follows this dashed path.

astronomers. Among his many accomplishments, Hipparchus developed the circle-upon-circle idea of Apollonius into a model that could predict planetary positions. To do this, Hipparchus had to add several features to the basic idea; for example, he included even smaller circles that moved upon the

original set of small circles, and he positioned the large circles slightly off-center from Earth.

Ptolemy's great accomplishment was to adapt and synthesize earlier ideas into a single system that agreed quite well with the astronomical observations available at the time. In the end, he created and published a model that could correctly forecast future planetary positions to within a few degrees of arc—roughly equivalent to the size of your hand viewed at arm's length against the sky. His model generally worked so well that it remained in use for the next 1500 years. When his book describing the model was translated by Arabic scholars around A.D. 800, they gave it the title *Almagest*, derived from words meaning "the greatest compilation."

How was Greek knowledge preserved through history?

One reason Greek thought gained such broad influence was that the Greeks proved as adept at politics and war as they were at philosophy. In about 330 B.C., Alexander the Great (356–323 B.C.) began a series of conquests that expanded the Greek Empire throughout the Middle East, absorbing the former empires of Egypt and Mesopotamia. Alexander was more than just a military leader. He was also keenly interested in science and education. As a teenager, he had been tutored by none other than Aristotle.

Alexander encouraged the pursuit of knowledge and respect for foreign cultures. On the Nile delta in Egypt, he founded the city of Alexandria, which soon became a center of world culture. Not long after his death, the city of Alexandria commenced work on a great library and research center: the Library of Alexandria, which opened in about

---

SPECIAL TOPIC

Eratosthenes Measures Earth

In a remarkable feat, the Greek scientist Eratosthenes accurately estimated the size of Earth in about 240 B.C. He did it by comparing the altitude of the Sun on the summer solstice in the Egyptian cities of Syene (modern-day Aswan) and Alexandria.

Eratosthenes knew that the Sun passed directly overhead in Syene on the summer solstice. He also knew that in Alexandria to the north, the Sun came within only 7° of the zenith on the summer solstice. He therefore reasoned that Alexandria must be 7° of latitude to the north of Syene (Figure 1). Because 7° is $\frac{7}{360}$ of a circle, he concluded that the north-south distance between Alexandria and Syene must be $\frac{7}{360}$ of the circumference of Earth.

Eratosthenes estimated the north-south distance between Syene and Alexandria to be 5000 stadia (the *stadium* was a Greek unit of distance). Thus, he concluded that

$$\frac{7}{360} \times \text{circumference of Earth} = 5000 \text{ stadia}$$

From this he found Earth's circumference to be about 250,000 stadia.

We don't know exactly what distance a stadium meant to Eratosthenes, but from sizes of actual Greek stadiums, it must have been about $\frac{1}{6}$ kilometer. Thus, Eratosthenes estimated the circumference of Earth to be about $\frac{250,000}{6}$ = 42,000 kilometers—impressively close to the real value of just over 40,000 kilometers.

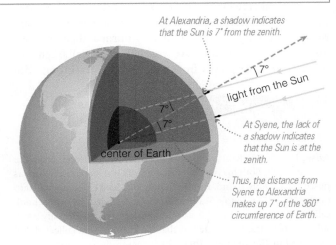

At Alexandria, a shadow indicates that the Sun is 7° from the zenith.

light from the Sun

center of Earth

At Syene, the lack of a shadow indicates that the Sun is at the zenith.

Thus, the distance from Syene to Alexandria makes up 7° of the 360° circumference of Earth.

FIGURE 1 At noon on the summer solstice, the Sun appears at the zenith in Syene but 7° shy of the zenith in Alexandria. Thus, 7° of latitude, which corresponds to a distance of $\frac{7}{360}$ of Earth's circumference, must separate the two cities.

a This rendering shows an artist's reconstruction of the Great Hall of the ancient Library of Alexandria.

b A rendering similar to (a), showing a scroll room in the ancient library.

c The New Library of Alexandria in Egypt, which opened in 2003.

FIGURE 3.16 The ancient Library of Alexandria thrived for some 700 years, starting in about 300 B.C.

300 B.C. (Figure 3.16). It remained the world's preeminent center of research for some 700 years, surviving well past the fall of the classical Greek Empire and into the heyday of the Roman Empire.

Destruction of the Library of Alexandria Much of the Library of Alexandria's long history remains unknown today, in part because the books that recorded this history were destroyed along with the library. Nevertheless, historians are confident that the library's demise was intertwined with the life and death of one of the few prominent female scholars of the ancient world: a woman named Hypatia (A.D. 370–415). Hypatia was one of the last resident scholars of the library, as well as the director of the observatory in Alexandria and one of the leading mathematicians and astronomers of her time. Unfortunately, she became a scapegoat during a time of rising sentiment against free inquiry and was murdered in A.D. 415. The final destruction of the library took place not long after her death.

At its peak, the Library of Alexandria may have held more than a half million books, handwritten on papyrus scrolls. Most of these scrolls were ultimately burned, their contents lost forever. In some cases, we were left with small fragments or titles or descriptions from other works, teasing us with

intriguing subject matter about which we will never read. In commemoration of the ancient library, Egypt built a New Library of Alexandria (the *Bibliotheca Alexandrina*, opened 2003), with hopes that it will once again make Alexandria a global center for scientific research.

THINK ABOUT IT

Estimate the number of books you're likely to read in your lifetime, and compare this number to the half million books once housed in the Library of Alexandria. Can you think of other ways to put into perspective the loss of ancient wisdom resulting from the destruction of the Library of Alexandria?

Islamic Preservation of Science Much of Greek knowledge was lost with the destruction of the Library of Alexandria. That which survived was preserved primarily thanks to the rise of a new center of intellectual inquiry in Baghdad (in present-day Iraq). While European civilization fell into the period of intellectual decline known as the Dark Ages, scholars of the new religion of Islam sought knowledge of mathematics and astronomy in hopes of better understanding the wisdom of Allah. During the 8th and 9th centuries A.D., scholars working in the Muslim Empire translated and thereby saved many ancient Greek works.

SPECIAL TOPIC

Aristotle

Aristotle (384–322 B.C.) is among the best-known philosophers of the ancient world. Both his parents died when he was a child, and he was raised by a family friend. In his 20s and 30s, he studied under Plato (428–348 B.C.) at Plato's Academy. He later founded his own school, called the Lyceum, where he studied and lectured on virtually every subject. Historical records tell us that his lectures were collected and published in 150 volumes. About 50 of these volumes survive to the present day.

Many of Aristotle's scientific discoveries were about the nature of plants and animals. He studied more than 500 animal species in detail, dissecting specimens of nearly 50 species, and came up with a strikingly modern classification system. For example, he was the first person to recognize that dolphins should be classified with land mammals

rather than with fish. In mathematics, he is known for laying the foundations of mathematical logic. Unfortunately, he was far less successful in physics and astronomy, areas in which many of his claims turned out to be wrong.

Despite his wide-ranging discoveries and writings, Aristotle's philosophies were not particularly influential until many centuries after his death. His books were preserved and valued by Islamic scholars but were unknown in Europe until they were translated into Latin in the 12th and 13th centuries. Aristotle's work gained great influence only after his philosophy was integrated into Christian theology by St. Thomas Aquinas (1225–1274). In the ancient world, Aristotle's greatest influence came indirectly, through his role as the tutor of Alexander the Great.

Around A.D. 800, the Islamic leader Al-Mamun (A.D. 786–833) established a "House of Wisdom" in Baghdad with a mission much like that of the destroyed Library of Alexandria. Founded in a spirit of openness and tolerance, the House of Wisdom employed Jews, Christians, and Muslims, all working together in scholarly pursuits. Using the translated Greek scientific manuscripts as building blocks, these scholars developed the mathematics of algebra and many new instruments and techniques for astronomical observation. Most of the official names of constellations and stars come from Arabic because of the work of the scholars at Baghdad. If you look at a star chart, you will see that the names of many bright stars begin with *al* (e.g., Aldebaran, Algol), which means "the" in Arabic.

Toward a Scientific Renaissance The Islamic world of the Middle Ages was in frequent contact with Hindu scholars from India, who in turn brought knowledge of ideas and discoveries from China. Hence, the intellectual center in Baghdad achieved a synthesis of the surviving work of the ancient Greeks and that of the Indians and the Chinese. The accumulated knowledge of the Arabs spread throughout the Byzantine empire (part of the former Roman Empire). When the Byzantine capital of Constantinople (modern-day Istanbul) fell to the Turks in 1453, many Eastern scholars headed west to Europe, carrying with them the knowledge that helped ignite the European Renaissance. It is to this story that we turn next in our quest to understand the origins of modern science.

3.3 THE COPERNICAN REVOLUTION

The Greeks and other ancient peoples developed many important scientific ideas, but what we now think of as science arose during the European Renaissance. Within a half century after the fall of Constantinople, Polish scientist Nicholas Copernicus began the work that ultimately overturned the Earth-centered Ptolemaic model. Over the next century and a half, philosophers and scientists (who were often one and the same) debated and tested his radical view of the cosmos. Ultimately, the new ideas introduced by Copernicus fundamentally changed the way we perceive our place in the universe. This dramatic change, known as the **Copernican revolution**, spurred the development of virtually all modern science and technology.

How did Copernicus, Tycho, and Kepler challenge the Earth-centered model?

The story of the Copernican revolution is in many ways the story of the origin of modern science. It is also the story of how three key individuals—Nicholas Copernicus, Tycho Brahe, and Johannes Kepler—challenged the prevailing dogma that our planet must be the center of the universe.

Copernicus Nicholas Copernicus was born in Toruń, Poland, on February 19, 1473. His family was wealthy and he received a first-class education in mathematics, medicine, and

law. He began studying astronomy in his late teens. By that time, tables of planetary motion based on the Ptolemaic model were noticeably inaccurate. But few people were willing to undertake the difficult calculations required to revise the tables. Indeed, the best tables available had been compiled some two centuries earlier under the guidance of Spanish monarch Alphonso X (1221–1284).

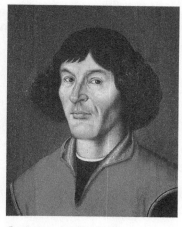

Copernicus (1473–1543)

Commenting on the tedious nature of the work required to make these *Alfonsine Tables,* the monarch is said to have complained, "If I had been present at the creation, I would have recommended a simpler design for the universe."

In his quest for a better way to predict planetary positions, Copernicus decided to try Aristarchus's Sun-centered idea, first proposed more than 1700 years earlier [Section 2.4]. He had read of Aristarchus's work, and recognized the much simpler explanation for apparent retrograde motion offered by a Sun-centered system (see Figure 2.33). But he went far beyond Aristarchus in working out mathematical details of the model. Through this process, Copernicus discovered simple geometric relationships that allowed him to calculate each planet's orbital period around the Sun and its relative distance from the Sun in terms of the Earth-Sun distance (see Mathematical Insight S1.1, p. 92). The model's success in providing a geometric layout for the solar system convinced him that the Sun-centered idea must be correct.

Despite his own confidence in the model, Copernicus was hesitant to publish his work, fearing that his suggestion that Earth moved would be considered absurd. However, he discussed his system with other scholars, including some high-ranking officials of the Catholic Church, who urged him to publish a book. Copernicus saw the first printed copy of his book, *De Revolutionibus Orbium Coelestium* ("Concerning the Revolutions of the Heavenly Spheres"), on the day he died—May 24, 1543.

Publication of the book spread the Sun-centered idea widely, and many scholars were drawn to the aesthetic advantages of his model. Nevertheless, the Copernican model gained relatively few converts over the next 50 years, for a good reason: It didn't work all that well. The primary problem was that while Copernicus had been willing to overturn Earth's central place in the cosmos, he had held fast to the ancient belief that heavenly motion must occur in perfect circles. This incorrect assumption forced him to add numerous complexities to his system (including circles on circles much like those used by Ptolemy) to get it to make decent predictions. In the end, his complete model was no more accurate and no less complex than the Ptolemaic model, and few people were willing to throw out thousands of years of tradition for a new model that worked just as poorly as the old one.

Tycho Part of the difficulty faced by astronomers who sought to improve either the Ptolemaic or the Copernican system was a lack of quality data. The telescope had not yet been invented, and existing naked-eye observations were not very accurate. Better data were needed, and they were provided by the Danish nobleman Tycho Brahe (1546–1601), usually known simply as Tycho (pronounced *tie-koe*).

Tycho became interested in astronomy as a young boy, but his family discouraged this interest. He therefore kept his passion secret, learning the constellations from a miniature model of a celestial sphere that he kept hidden. As he grew older, Tycho was often arrogant about both his noble birth and his intellectual abilities. At age 20, he fought a duel with another student over which of them was the better mathematician. Part of Tycho's nose was cut off, and he designed a replacement piece made of silver and gold.

Tycho Brahe (1546–1601)

In 1563, Tycho decided to observe a widely anticipated alignment of Jupiter and Saturn. To his surprise, the alignment occurred nearly 2 days later than the date Copernicus had predicted. Resolving to improve the state of astronomical prediction, he set about compiling careful observations of stellar and planetary positions in the sky.

Tycho's fame grew after he observed what he called a *nova*, meaning "new star," in 1572. By measuring its parallax and comparing it to the parallax of the Moon, he proved that the nova was much farther away than the Moon. (Today, we know that Tycho saw a *supernova*—the explosion of a distant star [Section 17.3].) In 1577, Tycho made similar observations of a comet and proved that it too lay in the realm of the heavens. Others, including Aristotle, had argued that comets were phenomena of Earth's atmosphere. King Frederick II of Denmark decided to sponsor Tycho's ongoing work, providing him with money to build an unparalleled observatory for naked-eye observations (Figure 3.17). After Frederick II died in 1588, Tycho moved to Prague, where German emperor Rudolf II supported his work.

Over a period of three decades, Tycho and his assistants compiled naked-eye observations accurate to within less than 1 arcminute—less than the thickness of a fingernail viewed at arm's length. Because the telescope was invented shortly after his death, Tycho's data remain the best set of naked-eye observations ever made. Despite the quality of his observations, Tycho never succeeded in coming up with a satisfying explanation for planetary motion. He was convinced that the *planets* must orbit the Sun, but his inability to detect stellar parallax [Section 2.4] led him to

FIGURE 3.17 Tycho Brahe in his naked-eye observatory, which worked much like a giant protractor. He could sit and observe a planet through the rectangular hole in the wall as an assistant used a sliding marker to measure the angle on the protractor.

conclude that Earth must remain stationary. He therefore advocated a model in which the Sun orbits Earth while all other planets orbit the Sun. Few people took this model seriously.

Kepler Tycho failed to explain the motions of the planets satisfactorily, but he succeeded in finding someone who could: In 1600, he hired the young German astronomer Johannes Kepler (1571–1630). Kepler and Tycho had a strained relationship, but Tycho recognized the talent of his young apprentice. In 1601, as he lay on his deathbed, Tycho begged Kepler

Johannes Kepler (1571–1630)

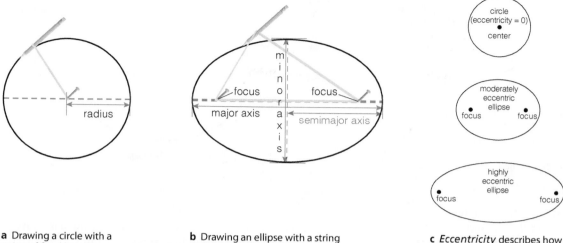

a Drawing a circle with a string of fixed length.

b Drawing an ellipse with a string of fixed length.

c *Eccentricity* describes how much an ellipse deviates from a perfect circle.

FIGURE 3.18 Interactive Figure An ellipse is a special type of oval. These diagrams show how an ellipse differs from a circle and how different ellipses vary in their eccentricity.

to find a system that would make sense of his observations so "that it may not appear I have lived in vain."*

Kepler was deeply religious and believed that understanding the geometry of the heavens would bring him closer to God. Like Copernicus, he believed that planetary orbits should be perfect circles, so he worked diligently to match circular motions to Tycho's data.

Kepler labored with particular intensity to find an orbit for Mars, which posed the greatest difficulties in matching the data to a circular orbit. After years of calculation, Kepler found a circular orbit that matched all of Tycho's observations of Mars's position along the ecliptic (east-west) to within 2 arcminutes. However, the model did not correctly predict Mars's positions north or south of the ecliptic. Because Kepler sought a physically realistic orbit for Mars, he could not (as Ptolemy and Copernicus had done) tolerate one model for the east-west positions and another for the north-south positions. He attempted to find a unified model with a circular orbit. In doing so, he found that some of his predictions differed from Tycho's observations by as much as 8 arcminutes.

Kepler surely was tempted to ignore these discrepancies and attribute them to errors by Tycho. After all, 8 arcminutes is barely one-fourth the angular diameter of the full moon. But Kepler trusted Tycho's careful work. The small discrepancies finally led Kepler to abandon the idea of circular orbits—and to find the correct solution to the ancient riddle of planetary motion. About this event, Kepler wrote:

If I had believed that we could ignore these eight minutes [of arc], I would have patched up my hypothesis accordingly. But, since it was not permissible to ignore, those eight minutes pointed the road to a complete reformation in astronomy.

---

*For a particularly moving version of the story of Tycho and Kepler, see Episode 3 of Carl Sagan's *Cosmos* video series.

Kepler's key discovery was that planetary orbits are not circles but instead are a special type of oval called an **ellipse.** You can draw a circle by putting a pencil on the end of a string, tacking the string to a board, and pulling the pencil around (Figure 3.18a). Drawing an ellipse is similar, except that you must stretch the string around *two* tacks (Figure 3.18b). The locations of the two tacks are called the **foci** (singular, **focus**) of the ellipse. The long axis of the ellipse is called its *major axis,* each half of which is called a **semimajor axis;** as we'll see shortly, the length of the semimajor axis is particularly important in astronomy. The short axis is called the *minor axis.* By altering the distance between the two foci while keeping the length of string the same, you can draw ellipses of varying **eccentricity,** a quantity that describes how much an ellipse is stretched out compared to a perfect circle (Figure 3.18c). A circle is an ellipse with zero eccentricity, and greater eccentricity means a more elongated ellipse.

Kepler's decision to trust the data over his preconceived beliefs marked an important transition point in the history of science. Once he abandoned perfect circles in favor of ellipses, Kepler soon came up with a model that could predict planetary positions with far greater accuracy than Ptolemy's Earth-centered model. Kepler's model withstood the test of time and became accepted not only as a model of nature but also as a deep, underlying truth about planetary motion.

MA Orbits and Kepler's Laws Tutorial, Lessons 2–4

What are Kepler's three laws of planetary motion?

Kepler summarized his discoveries with three simple laws that we now call **Kepler's laws of planetary motion.** He published the first two laws in 1609 and the third in 1619.

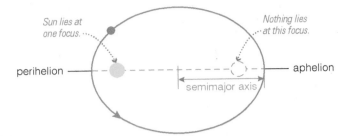

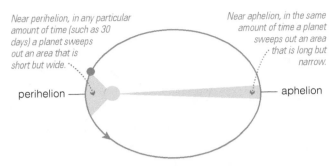

FIGURE 3.19 `Interactive Figure` Kepler's first law: The orbit of each planet about the Sun is an ellipse with the Sun at one focus. (The eccentricity shown here is exaggerated compared to the actual eccentricities of the planets.)

The areas swept out in 30-day periods are all equal.

FIGURE 3.20 `Interactive Figure` Kepler's second law: As a planet moves around its orbit, an imaginary line connecting it to the Sun sweeps out equal areas (the shaded regions) in equal times.

Kepler's First Law Kepler's first law tells us that *the orbit of each planet around the Sun is an ellipse with the Sun at one focus* (Figure 3.19). (Nothing is at the other focus.) In essence, this law tells us that a planet's distance from the Sun varies during its orbit. It is closest at the point called **perihelion** (from the Greek for "near the Sun") and farthest at the point called **aphelion** (from the Greek for "away from the Sun"). The *average* of a planet's perihelion and aphelion distances is the length of its *semimajor axis*. We will refer to this simply as the planet's average distance from the Sun.

Kepler's Second Law Kepler's second law states that *as a planet moves around its orbit, it sweeps out equal areas in equal times*. As shown in Figure 3.20, this means the planet moves a greater distance when it is near perihelion than it does in the same amount of time near aphelion. That is, the planet travels faster when it is nearer to the Sun and slower when it is farther from the Sun.

Kepler's Third Law Kepler's third law tells us that *more distant planets orbit the Sun at slower average speeds, obeying a precise mathematical relationship*. The relationship is written

$$p^2 = a^3$$

where p is the planet's orbital period in years and a is its average distance from the Sun in astronomical units. Figure 3.21a shows the $p^2 = a^3$ law graphically. Notice that the square of each planet's orbital period (p^2) is indeed equal to the cube of its average distance from the Sun (a^3). Because Kepler's third law relates a planet's orbital distance to its orbital time (period), we can use the law to calculate a planet's average orbital speed.* Figure 3.21b shows the result, confirming that more distant planets orbit the Sun more slowly.

The fact that more distant planets move more slowly led Kepler to suggest that planetary motion might be the result of a force from the Sun. He even speculated about the nature of this force, guessing that it might be related to magnetism. (This idea, shared by Galileo, was first suggested by William Gilbert [1544–1603], an early believer in the Copernican system.) Kepler was right about the existence of a force but wrong in his guess of magnetism. A half century later, Isaac

---

*To calculate orbital speed from Kepler's third law: Remember that speed = distance/time. For a planetary orbit, the distance is the orbital circumference, or $2\pi a$ (where a is the semimajor axis, roughly the "radius" of the orbit), and the time is the orbital period p, so the orbital speed is $(2\pi a)/p$. From Kepler's third law, $p = a^{3/2}$. Plugging this value for p into the orbital speed equation, we find that a planet's orbital speed is $2\pi/\sqrt{a}$; the graph of this equation is the curve in Figure 3.21b.

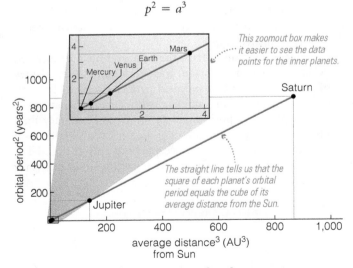

a This graph shows that Kepler's third law ($p^2 = a^3$) does indeed hold true; the graph shows only the planets known in Kepler's time.

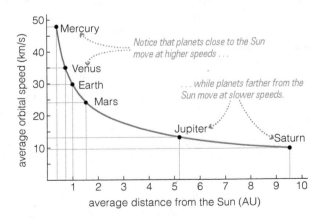

b This graph, based on Kepler's third law and modern values of planetary distances, shows that more distant planets orbit the Sun more slowly.

FIGURE 3.21 Graphs based on Kepler's third law.

Newton finally explained planetary motion as a consequence of gravity [Section 4.4].

THINK ABOUT IT

*S*uppose a comet has an orbit that brings it quite close to the Sun at its perihelion and beyond Mars at its aphelion, but with an average distance (semimajor axis) of 1 AU. According to Kepler's laws, how long does the comet take to complete each orbit? Does it spend most of its time close to the Sun, far from the Sun, or somewhere in between? Explain.

How did Galileo solidify the Copernican revolution?

The success of Kepler's laws in matching Tycho's data provided strong evidence in favor of Copernicus's placement of the Sun, rather than Earth, at the center of the solar system. Nevertheless, many scientists still voiced reasonable objections to the Copernican view. There were three basic objections, all rooted in the 2000-year-old beliefs of Aristotle and other ancient Greeks.

- First, Aristotle had held that Earth could not be moving because, if it were, objects such as birds, falling stones, and clouds would be left behind as Earth moved along its way.

- Second, the idea of noncircular orbits contradicted Aristotle's claim that the heavens—the realm of the Sun, Moon, planets, and stars—must be perfect and unchanging.

- Third, no one had detected the stellar parallax that should occur if Earth orbits the Sun [Section 2.4].

Galileo Galilei (1564–1642), usually known by only his first name, answered all three objections.

Galileo defused the first objection with experiments that almost single-handedly overturned the Aristotelian view of physics. In particular, he used experiments with rolling balls to demonstrate that a moving object remains in motion *unless* a force acts to stop it (an idea now codified in Newton's first law of motion [Section 4.2]). This insight explained why objects that share Earth's motion through space—such

---

MATHEMATICAL INSIGHT 3.1

Eccentricity and Planetary Orbits

We describe how much a planet's orbit differs from a perfect circle by stating its orbital *eccentricity*. There are several equivalent ways to define the eccentricity of an ellipse, but the simplest is shown in Figure 1. We define c to be the distance from each focus to the center of the ellipse and a to be the length of the semimajor axis. The eccentricity, e, is then defined to be

$$e = \frac{c}{a}$$

Notice that $c = 0$ for a perfect circle, because a circle is an ellipse with both foci *in* the center, so this formula gives an eccentricity of 0 for a perfect circle, just as we expect.

You can find the orbital eccentricities for the planets in tables such as Table E.2 in Appendix E of this book. Once you know the eccentricity, the following formulas allow you to calculate the planet's perihelion and aphelion distances (Figure 2):

$$\text{perihelion distance} = a(1 - e)$$
$$\text{aphelion distance} = a(1 + e)$$

EXAMPLE: What are Earth's perihelion and aphelion distances?

SOLUTION:

Step 1 Understand: To use the given formulas, we need to know Earth's orbital eccentricity and semimajor axis length. From Table E.2, Earth's orbital eccentricity is $e = 0.017$ and its semimajor axis (average distance from Sun) is 1 AU, or $a = 149.6$ million km.

Step 2 Solve: We plug these values into the equations:

Earth's perihelion distance $= a(1 - e)$

$= (149.6 \times 10^6 \text{ km})(1 - 0.017)$

$= 147.1 \times 10^6 \text{ km}$

Earth's aphelion distance $= a(1 + e)$

$= (149.6 \times 10^6 \text{ km})(1 + 0.017)$

$= 152.1 \times 10^6 \text{ km}$

Step 3 Explain: Earth's perihelion (nearest to Sun) distance is 147.1 million kilometers and its aphelion (farthest from Sun) distance is 152.1 million kilometers. In other words, Earth's distance from the Sun varies between 147.1 and 152.1 million kilometers.

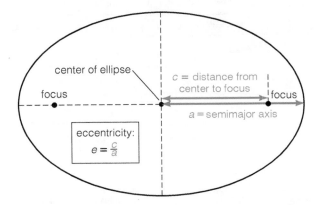

FIGURE 1

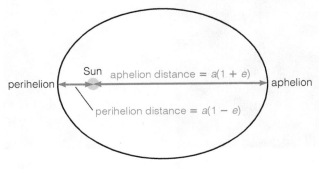

FIGURE 2

as birds, falling stones, and clouds—should *stay* with Earth rather than falling behind as Aristotle had argued. This same idea explains why passengers stay with a moving airplane even when they leave their seats.

Tycho's supernova and comet observations already had challenged the validity of the second objection by showing that the heavens could change. Galileo shattered the idea of heavenly perfection after he built a telescope in late 1609. (Galileo did *not* patent the telescope; Hans Lippershey patented it in 1608. However, Galileo took what was little more than a toy and turned it into a scientific instrument.) Through his telescope, Galileo saw sunspots on the Sun, which were considered "imperfections" at the time. He also used his telescope to prove that the Moon has mountains and valleys like the "imperfect" Earth by noticing the shadows cast near the dividing line between the light and dark portions of the lunar face (Figure 3.22). If the heavens were in fact not perfect, then the idea of elliptical orbits (as opposed to "perfect" circles) was not so objectionable.

Galileo (1564–1642)

The third objection—the absence of observable stellar parallax—had been of particular concern to Tycho. Based on his estimates of the distances of stars, Tycho believed that his naked-eye observations were sufficiently precise to detect stellar parallax if Earth did in fact orbit the Sun. Refuting Tycho's argument required showing that the stars were more distant than Tycho had thought and therefore too distant for him to have observed stellar parallax. Although Galileo didn't actually prove this fact, he provided strong evidence in its favor. For example, he saw with his telescope that the Milky Way resolved into countless individual stars. This discovery helped him argue that the stars were far more numerous and more distant than Tycho had believed.

In hindsight, the final nails in the coffin of the Earth-centered model came with two of Galileo's earliest discoveries through the telescope. First, he observed four moons clearly orbiting Jupiter, *not* Earth (Figure 3.23). By itself, this observation still did not rule out a stationary, central Earth. However, it showed that moons can orbit a moving planet like Jupiter, which overcame some critics' complaints that the Moon could not stay with a moving Earth. Soon thereafter, he observed that Venus goes through phases in a way that makes sense only if it orbits the Sun and not Earth (Figure 3.24).

With Earth clearly removed from its position at the center of the universe, the scientific debate turned to the question of whether Kepler's laws were the correct model for our solar system. The most convincing evidence came in 1631, when astronomers observed a transit of Mercury across the Sun's face. Kepler's laws had predicted the transit with overwhelmingly better success than any competing model.

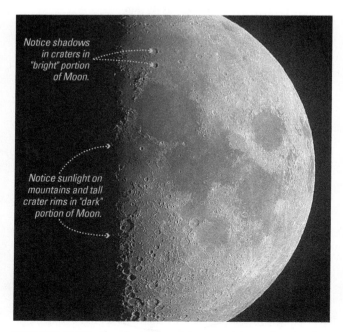

FIGURE 3.22 The shadows cast by mountains and crater rims near the dividing line between the light and dark portions of the lunar face prove that the Moon's surface is not perfectly smooth.

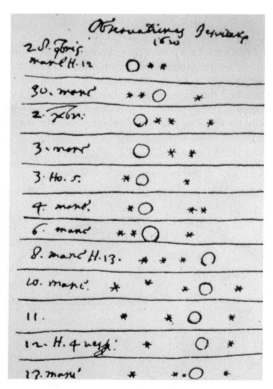

FIGURE 3.23 A page from Galileo's notebook written in 1610. His sketches show four "stars" near Jupiter (the circle) but in different positions at different times (and sometimes hidden from view). Galileo soon realized that the "stars" were actually moons orbiting Jupiter.

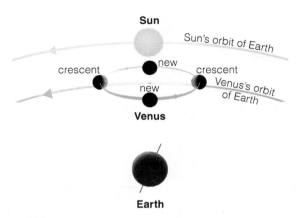

Ptolemaic View of Venus

a In the Ptolemaic system, Venus orbits Earth, moving around a smaller circle on its larger orbital circle; the center of the smaller circle lies on the Earth-Sun line. If this view were correct, Venus's phases would range only from new to crescent.

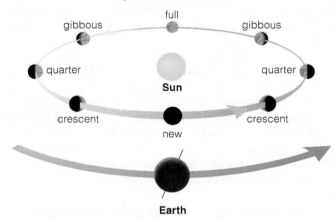

Copernican View of Venus

b In reality, Venus orbits the Sun, so from Earth we can see it in many different phases. This is just what Galileo observed, allowing him to prove that Venus orbits the Sun.

FIGURE 3.24 Interactive Figure Galileo's telescopic observations of Venus proved that it orbits the Sun rather than Earth.

Although we now recognize that Galileo won the day, the story was more complex in his own time, when Catholic Church doctrine still held Earth to be the center of the universe. On June 22, 1633, Galileo was brought before a Church inquisition in Rome and ordered to recant his claim that Earth orbits the Sun. Nearly 70 years old and fearing for his life, Galileo did as ordered and his life was spared. However, legend has it that as he rose from his knees he

---

MATHEMATICAL INSIGHT 3.2

Kepler's Third Law

When Kepler discovered his third law, $p^2 = a^3$, he knew only that it applied to the orbits of planets around the Sun. In fact, it applies much more generally. For example, it works for asteroids and comets as well as planets. We'll see its most general form in Mathematical Insight 4.3, but even in its original form we can use Kepler's third law for any object *if*

1. the object is *orbiting the Sun* or another star of precisely the same mass as the Sun and
2. we measure orbital *periods in years* and orbital *distances in AU*.

EXAMPLE 1: The largest asteroid, Ceres, orbits the Sun at an average distance (semimajor axis) of 2.77 AU. What is its orbital period?

SOLUTION:

Step 1 Understand: Kepler's third law will allow us to find the orbital period (p) from the average distance (a) if both conditions above are met. For Ceres, the first condition is met because it orbits the Sun and the second is met because we are given the orbital distance in AU. We therefore can use Kepler's third law in its original form.

Step 2 Solve: Kepler's third law is written in a form that gives us p^2, so to find the orbital period p we first solve the equation for p and then substitute the given value of $a = 2.77$ AU.

$$p^2 = a^3 \Rightarrow p = \sqrt{a^3} = \sqrt{2.77^3} = 4.6$$

Notice that because of the special conditions attached to the use of Kepler's third law in its original form, we do *not* include units

when working with it; we know we'll get a period in years as long as we start with a distance in AU.

Step 3 Explain: Ceres has an orbital period of 4.6 years, meaning it takes 4.6 years to complete each orbit around the Sun.

EXAMPLE 2: A new planet is discovered to be orbiting a star with the same mass as our Sun. The planet orbits the star every 3 months. What is its average distance from its star?

SOLUTION:

Step 1 Understand: This time we are given an orbital period and want to find the orbital distance. Again, we can use Kepler's third law in its original form only if the problem meets the two conditions above. The first condition is met because the planet is orbiting a star with the same mass as our Sun. The second is not met, because the orbital period is given in months rather than years. However, we can easily convert it to years: Three months is $\frac{1}{4}$ year, so we have $p = 0.25$ year.

Step 2 Solve: Kepler's law is written in a form that gives us a^2, so we solve the equation for a and then substitute the orbital period of $p = 0.25$ year:

$$p^2 = a^3 \Rightarrow a = \sqrt[3]{p^2} = \sqrt[3]{0.25^2} = 0.40$$

Step 3 Explain: The planet orbits its star at an average distance of 0.4 AU. By comparing this result to the distances of planets in our own solar system given in Table E.2, we find that this planet's average orbital distance is just slightly larger than that of the planet Mercury in our own solar system.

whispered under his breath, *Eppur si muove*—Italian for "And yet it moves." (Given the likely consequences if Church officials had heard him say this, most historians doubt the legend; see Special Topic, p. 78.)

The Church did not formally vindicate Galileo until 1992, but Church officials gave up the argument long before that: In 1757, all works backing the idea of a Sun-centered solar system were removed from the Church's index of banned books. Today, Catholic scientists are at the forefront of much astronomical research, and official Church teachings are compatible not only with Earth's planetary status but also with the theories of the Big Bang and the subsequent evolution of the cosmos and of life.

3.4 THE NATURE OF SCIENCE

The story of how our ancestors gradually figured out the basic architecture of the cosmos exhibits many features of what we now consider "good science." For example, we have seen how models were formulated and tested against observations and modified or replaced when they failed those tests. The story also illustrates some classic mistakes, such as the apparent failure of anyone before Kepler to question the belief that orbits must be circles. The ultimate success of the Copernican revolution led scientists, philosophers, and theologians to reassess the various modes of thinking that played a role in the 2000-year process of discovering Earth's place in the universe. Let's examine how the principles of modern science emerged from the lessons learned in the Copernican revolution.

How can we distinguish science from nonscience?

It's surprisingly difficult to define the term *science* precisely. The word comes from the Latin *scientia,* meaning "knowledge," but not all knowledge is science. For example, you may know what music you like best, but your musical taste is not a result of scientific study.

The Idealized Scientific Method One reason science is difficult to define is that not all science works in the same way. For example, you've probably heard that science is supposed to proceed according to something called the "scientific method." As an idealized illustration of this method, consider what you would do if your flashlight suddenly stopped working. In hopes of fixing the flashlight, you might *hypothesize* that its batteries have died. This type of tentative explanation, or **hypothesis**, is sometimes called an *educated guess*—in this case, it is "educated" because you already know that flashlights need batteries. Your hypothesis allows you to make a simple prediction: If you replace the batteries with new ones, the flashlight should work. You can test this prediction by replacing the batteries. If the flashlight now works, you've confirmed your hypothesis. If it doesn't, you must revise or discard your hypothesis, perhaps in favor of some other one that you can also test (such as that the bulb is burned out). Figure 3.25 illustrates the basic flow of this process.

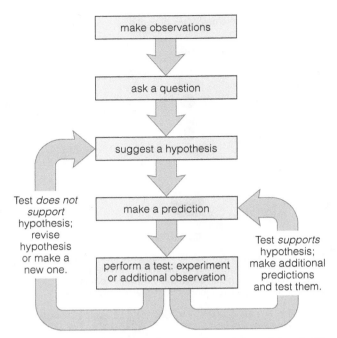

FIGURE 3.25 This diagram illustrates what we often call the scientific method.

The scientific method can be a useful idealization, but real science rarely progresses in such an orderly way. Scientific progress often begins with someone going out and looking at nature in a general way, rather than by conducting a careful set of experiments. For example, Galileo wasn't looking for anything in particular when he pointed his telescope at the sky and made his first startling discoveries. Furthermore, scientists are human beings, and their intuition and personal beliefs inevitably influence their work. Copernicus, for example, adopted the idea that Earth orbits the Sun not because he had carefully tested it but because he believed it made more sense than the prevailing view of an Earth-centered universe. While his intuition guided him to the right general idea, he erred in the specifics because he still held Plato's ancient belief that heavenly motion must be in perfect circles.

Given that the idealized scientific method is an overly simplistic characterization of science, how can we tell what is science and what is not? To answer this question, we must look a little deeper at the distinguishing characteristics of scientific thinking.

Hallmarks of Science One way to define scientific thinking is to list the criteria that scientists use when they judge competing models of nature. Historians and philosophers of science have examined (and continue to examine) this issue in great depth, and different experts express different viewpoints on the details. Nevertheless, everything we now consider to be science shares the following three basic characteristics, which we will refer to as the "hallmarks" of science (Figure 3.26):

■ Modern science seeks explanations for observed phenomena that rely solely on natural causes.

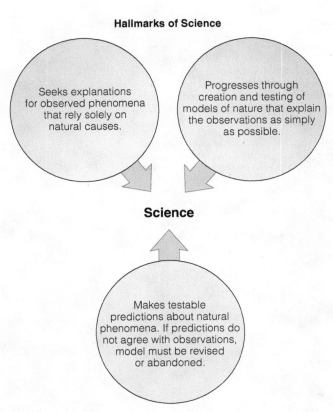

Hallmarks of Science

Seeks explanations for observed phenomena that rely solely on natural causes.

Progresses through creation and testing of models of nature that explain the observations as simply as possible.

Science

Makes testable predictions about natural phenomena. If predictions do not agree with observations, model must be revised or abandoned.

FIGURE 3.26 Hallmarks of science.

- Science progresses through the creation and testing of models of nature that explain the observations as simply as possible.

- A scientific model must make testable predictions about natural phenomena that will force us to revise or abandon the model if the predictions do not agree with observations.

Each of these hallmarks is evident in the story of the Copernican revolution. The first shows up in the way Tycho's careful measurements of planetary motion motivated Kepler to come up with a better explanation for those motions. The second is evident in the way several competing models were compared and tested, most notably those of Ptolemy, Copernicus, and Kepler. We see the third in the fact that each model could make precise predictions about the future motions of the Sun, Moon, planets, and stars in our sky. When a model's predictions failed, the model was modified or ultimately discarded. Kepler's model gained acceptance in large part because its predictions were so much better than those of the Ptolemaic model in matching Tycho's observations. The Cosmic Context spread in Figure 3.27 summarizes the key scientific changes that occurred with the Copernican revolution and how they illustrate the hallmarks of science.

Occam's Razor The criterion of simplicity in the second hallmark deserves additional explanation. Remember that the original model of Copernicus did *not* match the data noticeably better than Ptolemy's model. If scientists had judged

Copernicus's model solely on the accuracy of its predictions, they might have rejected it immediately. However, many scientists found elements of the Copernican model appealing, such as its simple explanation for apparent retrograde motion. They therefore kept the model alive until Kepler found a way to make it work.

In fact, if agreement with data were the sole criterion for judgment, we could imagine a modern-day Ptolemy adding millions or billions of additional circles to the geocentric model in an effort to improve its agreement with observations. A sufficiently complex geocentric model could in principle reproduce the observations with almost perfect accuracy—but it still would not convince us that Earth is the center of the universe. We would still choose the Copernican view over the geocentric view because its predictions would be just as accurate but follow a much simpler model of nature. The idea that scientists should prefer the simpler of two models that agree equally well with observations is called *Occam's razor*, after the medieval scholar William of Occam (1285–1349).

Verifiable Observations The third hallmark of science forces us to face the question of what counts as an "observation" against which a prediction can be tested. Consider the claim that aliens are visiting Earth in UFOs. Proponents of this claim say that thousands of eyewitness observations of UFO encounters provide evidence that it is true. But do these personal testimonials count as *scientific* evidence? On the surface, the answer isn't obvious, because all scientific studies involve eyewitness accounts on some level. For example, only a handful of scientists have personally made detailed tests of Einstein's theory of relativity, and it is their personal reports of the results that have convinced other scientists of the theory's validity. However, there's an important difference between personal testimony about a scientific test and an observation of a UFO: The first can be verified by anyone, at least in principle, while the second cannot.

Understanding this difference is crucial to understanding what counts as science and what does not. Even though you may never have conducted a test of Einstein's theory of relativity yourself, there's nothing stopping you from doing so. It might require several years of study before you have the necessary background to conduct the test, but you could then confirm the results reported by other scientists. In other words, while you may currently be trusting the eyewitness testimony of scientists, you always have the option of verifying their testimony for yourself.

In contrast, there is no way for you to verify someone's eyewitness account of a UFO. Without hard evidence such as photographs or pieces of the UFO, there is nothing that you could evaluate for yourself, even in principle. (And in those cases where "hard evidence" for UFO sightings has been presented, scientific study has never yet found the evidence to be strong enough to support the claim of alien spacecraft [Section 24.5].) Moreover, scientific studies of eyewitness testimony show it to be notoriously unreliable, because different eyewitnesses often disagree on what they saw even immediately after an event has occurred. As time passes, memories of the event may change further. In some cases in which memory

Ancient Earth-centered models of the universe easily explained the simple motions of the Sun and Moon through our sky, but had difficulty explaining the more complicated motions of the planets. The quest to understand planetary motions ultimately led to a revolution in our thinking about Earth's place in the universe that illustrates the process of science. This figure summarizes the major steps in that process.

(1) Night-by-night, planets usually move from west to east relative to the stars. However, during periods of *apparent retrograde motion,* they reverse direction for a few weeks to months [Section 2.4]. The ancient Greeks knew that any credible model of the solar system had to explain these observations.

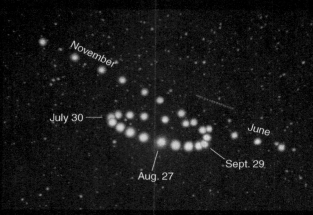

This composite photo shows the apparent retrograde motion of Mars.

(2) Most ancient Greek thinkers assumed that Earth remained fixed at the center of the solar system. To explain retrograde motion, they therefore added a complicated scheme of circles moving upon circles to their Earth-centered model. However, at least some Greeks, such as Aristarchus, preferred a Sun-centered model, which offered a simpler explanation for retrograde motion.

The Greek geocentric model explained apparent retrograde motion by having planets move around Earth on small circles that turned on larger circles.

HALLMARK OF SCIENCE **A scientific model must seek explanations for observed phenomena that rely solely on natural causes.** The ancient Greeks used geometry to explain their observations of planetary motion.

(Left page)
A schematic map of the universe from 1539 with Earth at the center and the Sun (Solis) orbiting it between Venus (Veneris) and Mars (Martis).

(Right page)
A page from Copernicus's De Revolutionibus, published in 1543, showing the Sun (Sol) at the center and Earth (Terra) orbiting between Venus and Mars.

③ By the time of Copernicus (1473–1543), predictions based on the Earth-centered model had become noticeably inaccurate. Hoping for improvement, Copernicus revived the Sun-centered idea. He did not succeed in making substantially better predictions because he retained the ancient belief that planets must move in perfect circles, but he inspired a revolution continued over the next century by Tycho, Kepler, and Galileo.

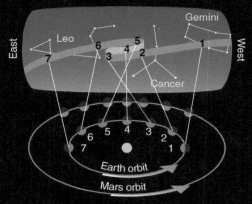

Apparent retrograde motion is simply explained in a Sun-centered system. Notice how Mars appears to change direction as Earth moves past it.

HALLMARK OF SCIENCE **Science progresses through creation and testing of models of nature that explain the observations as simply as possible.** Copernicus developed a Sun-centered model in hopes of explaining observations better than the more complicated Earth-centered model.

④ Tycho exposed flaws in both the ancient Greek and Copernican models by observing planetary motions with unprecedented accuracy. His observations led to Kepler's breakthrough insight that planetary orbits are elliptical, not circular, and enabled Kepler to develop his three laws of planetary motion.

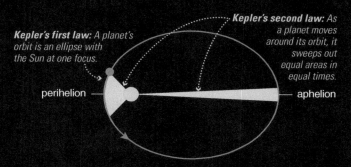

Kepler's first law: A planet's orbit is an ellipse with the Sun at one focus.

Kepler's second law: As a planet moves around its orbit, it sweeps out equal areas in equal times.

perihelion — aphelion

Kepler's third law: More distant planets orbit at slower average speeds, obeying $p^2 = a^3$.

HALLMARK OF SCIENCE **A scientific model makes testable predictions about natural phenomena. If predictions do not agree with observations, the model must be revised or abandoned.** Kepler could not make his model agree with observations until he abandoned the belief that planets move in perfect circles.

⑤ Galileo's experiments and telescopic observations overcame remaining scientific objections to the Sun-centered model. Together, Galileo's discoveries and the success of Kepler's laws in predicting planetary motion overthrew the Earth-centered model once and for all.

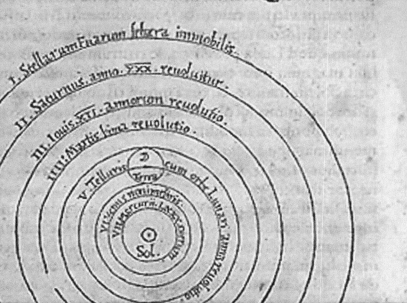

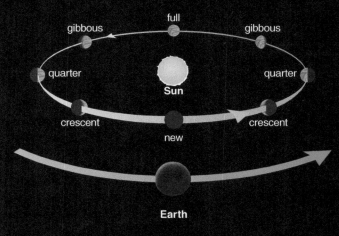

With his telescope, Galileo saw phases of Venus that are consistent only with the idea that Venus orbits the Sun rather than Earth.

has been checked against reality, people have reported vivid memories of events that never happened at all. This explains something that virtually all of us have experienced: disagreements with a friend about who did what and when. Since both people cannot be right in such cases, at least one person must have a memory that differs from reality.

Because of its demonstrated unreliability, eyewitness testimony alone cannot be used as evidence in science, no matter who reports it or how many people offer similar testimony. It can be used in support of a scientific model only when it is backed up by independently verifiable evidence that anyone could in principle check. (For much the same reason, eyewitness testimony is usually insufficient for a conviction in criminal court; additional evidence is required.)

Science and Pseudoscience It's important to realize that science is not the only valid way of seeking knowledge.

For example, suppose you are shopping for a car, learning to play drums, or pondering the meaning of life. In each case, you might make observations, exercise logic, and test hypotheses. Yet these pursuits clearly are not science, because they are not directed at developing testable explanations for observed natural phenomena. As long as nonscientific searches for knowledge make no claims about how the natural world works, they do not conflict with science.

However, you will often hear claims about the natural world that seem to be based on observational evidence but do not treat evidence in a truly scientific way. Such claims are often called **pseudoscience**, which literally means "false science." To distinguish real science from pseudoscience, a good first step is to check whether a particular claim exhibits all three hallmarks of science. Consider the example of people who claim a psychic ability to "see" the future and use it to make specific, testable predictions. In this sense, "seeing" the future sounds scientific,

SPECIAL TOPIC

And Yet It Moves

The case of Galileo is often portrayed as a simple example of conflict between science and religion, but the reality was much more complex, with deep divisions inside the Church hierarchy. Perhaps the clearest evidence for a more open-minded Church comes from the case of Copernicus, whose revolutionary work was strongly supported by many Church officials. A less-well-known and even earlier example concerns Nicholas of Cusa (1401–1464), who published a book arguing for a Sun-centered solar system in 1440, more than a century before Copernicus. Nicholas was ordained a priest in the same year that his book was published, and he was later elevated to Cardinal. Clearly, his views caused no problems for Church officials of the time. (Copernicus probably was not aware of this work by Nicholas of Cusa.)

Many other scientists received similar support from within the Church. Indeed, for most of his life, Galileo counted Cardinals (and even the Pope who later excommunicated him) among his friends. Some historians suspect that Galileo got into trouble less for his views than for the way in which he portrayed them. For example, in 1632—just a year before his famous trial—he published a book in which two fictional characters debated the geocentric and Sun-centered views. He named the character taking the geocentric position Simplicio—essentially "simple-minded"—and someone apparently convinced the Pope that the character was meant to represent him. If it was personality rather than belief that got Galileo into trouble, he was not the only one. Another early supporter of Copernicus, Giordano Bruno (1548–1600), drew the wrath of the Church after essentially writing that no rational person could disagree with him (not just on the Copernican system but on other matters as well). Bruno was branded a heretic and burned at the stake.

The evidence supporting the idea that Earth rotates and orbits the Sun was quite strong by the time of Galileo's trial in 1633, but it was still indirect. Thus, conservatives within the Church could at least make some case against Galileo. Today, we have much more direct proof that Galileo was correct when he supposedly whispered of Earth, *Eppur si muove*—"And yet it moves."

French physicist Jean Foucault provided the first direct proof of *rotation* in 1851. Foucault built a large pendulum that he carefully started swinging. Any pendulum tends to swing always in the same plane, but Earth's rotation made Foucault's pendulum appear to twist

slowly in a circle. Today, *Foucault pendulums* are a popular attraction at many science centers and museums (Figure 1). A second direct proof that Earth rotates is provided by the *Coriolis effect,* first described by French physicist Gustave Coriolis (1792–1843). The Coriolis effect [Section 10.2], which would not occur if Earth were not rotating, is responsible for things such as the swirling of hurricanes and the fact that missiles that travel great distances on Earth deviate from straight-line paths.

The first direct proof that Earth orbits the Sun came from English astronomer James Bradley (1693–1762). To understand Bradley's proof, imagine that starlight is like rain, falling straight down. If you are standing still, you should hold your umbrella straight over your head, but if you are walking through the rain, you should tilt your umbrella forward, because your motion makes the rain appear to be coming down at an angle. Bradley discovered that observing light from stars requires that telescopes be tilted slightly in the direction of Earth's motion—just like the umbrella. This effect is called the *aberration of starlight.* Stellar parallax also provides direct proof that Earth orbits the Sun, and it was first measured in 1838 by German astronomer Friedrich Bessel.

FIGURE 1 A Foucault pendulum at the Science Museum of Virginia.

since we can test it. However, numerous studies have tested the predictions of "seers" and have found that their predictions come true no more often than would be expected by pure chance. If the "seers" were scientific, they would admit that this evidence undercuts their claim of psychic abilities. Instead, they generally make excuses, such as saying that the predictions didn't come true because of "psychic interference." Making testable claims but then ignoring the results of the tests marks the claimed ability to see the future as pseudoscience.

Objectivity in Science The idea that science is objective, meaning that all people should be able to find the same results, is very important to the validity of science as a means of seeking knowledge. However, there is a difference between the overall objectivity of science and the objectivity of individual scientists. Because science is practiced by human beings, individual scientists bring their personal biases and beliefs to their scientific work.

Personal bias can influence the way a scientist proposes or tests a model. For example, most scientists choose their research projects based on personal interests rather than on some objective formula. In some extreme cases, scientists have even been known to cheat—either deliberately or subconsciously—to obtain a result they desire. For example, a little over a century ago, astronomer Percival Lowell claimed to see a network of artificial canals in blurry telescopic images of Mars, leading him to conclude that there was a great Martian civilization [Section 9.4]. But no such canals actually exist, so Lowell must have allowed his beliefs about extraterrestrial life to influence the way he interpreted what he saw—in essence, a form of cheating, though probably not intentional.

Bias can sometimes show up even in the thinking of the scientific community as a whole. Some valid ideas may not be considered by any scientist because the ideas fall too far outside

the general patterns of thought, or **paradigm**, of the time. Einstein's theory of relativity provides an example. Many scientists in the decades before Einstein had gleaned hints of the theory but did not investigate them, at least in part because they seemed too outlandish. (Chapters S2 and S3 discuss Einstein's special and general theories of relativity.)

The beauty of science is that it encourages continued testing by many people. Even if personal biases affect some results, tests by others should eventually uncover the mistakes. Similarly, if a new idea is correct but falls outside the accepted paradigm, sufficient testing and verification of the idea will eventually force a shift in the paradigm. In that sense, science ultimately provides a means of bringing people to agreement, at least on topics that can be subjected to scientific study.

What is a scientific theory?

The most successful scientific models explain a wide variety of observations in terms of just a few general principles. When a powerful yet simple model makes predictions that survive repeated and varied testing, scientists elevate its status and call it a **theory**. Some famous examples are Isaac Newton's theory of gravity, Charles Darwin's theory of evolution, and Albert Einstein's theory of relativity.

Note that the scientific meaning of the word *theory* is quite different from its everyday meaning, in which we equate a theory more closely with speculation or a hypothesis. For example, someone might get a new idea and say "I have a new theory about why people enjoy the beach." Without the support of a broad range of evidence that others have tested and confirmed, this "theory" is really only a guess. In contrast, Newton's theory of gravity qualifies as a scientific theory because it uses simple physical principles to explain many observations and experiments.

Despite its success in explaining observed phenomena, a scientific theory can never be proved true beyond all doubt, because future observations may disagree with its predictions. However, anything that qualifies as a scientific theory must be supported by a large, compelling body of evidence.

In this sense, a scientific theory is not at all like a hypothesis or any other type of guess. We are free to change a hypothesis at any time, because it has not yet been carefully tested. In contrast, we can discard or replace a scientific theory only if we have an alternative way of explaining the evidence that supports it.

Again, the theories of Newton and Einstein offer good examples. A vast body of evidence supports Newton's theory of gravity, but in the late 19th century scientists began to discover cases where its predictions did not perfectly match observations. These discrepancies were explained only when Einstein developed his general theory of relativity in the early 20th century. Still, the many successes of Newton's theory could not be ignored, and Einstein's theory would not have gained acceptance if it had not been able to explain these successes equally well. It did, and that is why we now view Einstein's theory as a broader theory of gravity than Newton's theory. Some scientists today are seeking a theory of gravity

Eggs on the Equinox

One of the hallmarks of science holds that you needn't take scientific claims on faith. In principle, at least, you can always test them for yourself. Consider the claim, repeated in news reports every year, that the spring equinox is the only day on which you can balance an egg on its end. Many people believe this claim, but you'll be immediately skeptical if you think about the nature of the spring equinox. The equinox is merely a point in time at which sunlight strikes both hemispheres equally (see Figure 2.15). It's difficult to see how sunlight could affect an attempt to balance eggs (especially if the eggs are indoors), and there is no difference in the strength of either Earth's gravity or the Sun's gravity on that day compared to any other day.

More important, you can test this claim directly. It's not easy to balance an egg on its end, but with practice you can do it on any day of the year, not just on the spring equinox. Not all scientific claims are so easy to test for yourself, but the basic lesson should be clear: Before you accept any scientific claim, you should demand at least a reasonable explanation of the evidence that backs it up.

In science, we attempt to acquire knowledge through logical reasoning. A logical argument begins with a set of premises and leads to one or more conclusions. Note that logical argument therefore differs somewhat from the definition of argument in everyday life, since logical arguments need not imply any animosity. There are two basic types of logical argument: *deductive* and *inductive*. Both are important in science.

In a deductive argument, the conclusion follows automatically from the premises, as in this example:

> PREMISE: All planets orbit the Sun in ellipses with the Sun at one focus.
>
> PREMISE: Earth is a planet.
>
> CONCLUSION: Earth orbits the Sun in an ellipse with the Sun at one focus.

Note the construction of the deductive argument: The first premise is a general statement that applies to all planets, and the conclusion is a specific statement that applies only to Earth. As this example suggests, we often use deduction to *deduce* a specific prediction from a more general theory. If the specific prediction proves to be false, then something must be wrong with the premises from which it was deduced. If it proves true, then we've acquired a piece of evidence in support of the premises.

Now, contrast the deductive argument above with the following example of an *inductive argument:*

> PREMISE: Birds fly up into the air but eventually come back down.
>
> PREMISE: People who jump into the air fall back down.
>
> PREMISE: Rocks thrown into the air come back down.
>
> PREMISE: Balls thrown into the air come back down.
>
> CONCLUSION: What goes up must come down.

Because each premise supports the conclusion, you might at first think that this is a strong inductive argument and that its conclusion probably is true. However, no matter how many more examples you consider of objects that go up and come down, you could never *prove* that the conclusion is true—only that it seems likely to be true. Moreover, a single counterexample can prove the conclusion of an inductive argument to be false. For example, in this case we know that the conclusion is false because the spacecraft *Voyager 2* was launched from Earth and never fell back down.

Inductive arguments *generalize* from specific facts to a broader model or theory. Thus, inductive arguments are the arguments used to build scientific theories, because we use them to *infer* general principles from observations and experiments. That is why theories can never be proved true beyond all doubt—they can only be shown to be consistent with ever larger bodies of evidence. Theories *can* be proved false, however, if they fail to account for observed or experimental facts.

---

that will go beyond Einstein's. If any new theory ever gains acceptance, it will have to match all the successes of Einstein's theory as well as work in new realms where Einstein's theory does not.

> **THINK ABOUT IT**
>
> When people claim that something is "only a theory," what do you think they mean? Does this meaning of "theory" agree with the definition of a theory in science? Do scientists always use the word *theory* in its "scientific" sense? Explain.

3.5 ASTROLOGY

We have discussed the development of astronomy and the nature of science in some depth. Now let's talk a little about a subject often confused with the science of astronomy: *astrology*. Although the terms *astrology* and *astronomy* sound very similar, today they describe very different practices. In ancient times, however, astrology and astronomy often went hand in hand, and astrology played an important role in the historical development of astronomy.

How is astrology different from astronomy?

The basic tenet of astrology is that the apparent positions of the Sun, Moon, and planets among the stars in our sky influence human events. The origins of this idea are easy to understand. After all, the position of the Sun in the sky certainly influences our lives, since it determines the seasons and the times of daylight and darkness, and the Moon's position determines the tides. It probably therefore seemed natural to imagine that planets—which are the only other objects to move among the stars besides the Sun and Moon—should also influence our lives, even if these influences were more subtle.

Ancient astrologers hoped to learn how the positions of the Sun, Moon, and planets influence our lives by charting the skies and seeking correlations with events on Earth. For example, if an earthquake occurred when Saturn was entering the constellation Leo, might Saturn's position have been the cause of the earthquake? If the king became ill when Mars appeared in the constellation Gemini and the first-quarter moon appeared in Scorpio, might it mean another tragedy for the king when this particular alignment of the Moon and Mars next recurred? Surely, the ancient astrologers thought, the patterns of influence would eventually become clear, and they would then be able to forecast human events with the same reliability with which astronomical observations of the Sun could forecast the coming of spring.

Because forecasts of the seasons and forecasts of human events were imagined to be closely related, astrologers and astronomers usually were one and the same in the ancient world. For example, in addition to his books on astronomy, Ptolemy published a treatise on astrology called *Tetrabiblios* that remains the foundation for much of astrology today. But Ptolemy himself recognized that astrology stood upon a far shakier foundation than astronomy. In the introduction to *Tetrabiblos*, Ptolemy compared astronomical and astrological predictions:

> [Astronomy], which is first both in order and effectiveness, is that whereby we apprehend the aspects of the movements of sun, moon, and stars in relation to each other and to the earth.... I shall now give an account of the second and less sufficient method [of prediction (astrology)] in a proper philosophical way, so that one whose aim is the truth might never compare its perceptions with the sureness of the first, unvarying science....

Other ancient scientists surely also recognized that their astrological predictions were far less reliable than their astronomical ones. Nevertheless, if there were even a slight possibility that astrologers could forecast the future, no king or political leader would dare to be without one. Astrologers held esteemed positions as political advisers in the ancient world and were provided with the resources they needed to continue charting the heavens and human history. Indeed, wealthy political leaders' support of astrology made possible much of the development of ancient astronomy.

Throughout the Middle Ages and into the Renaissance, many astronomers continued to practice astrology. For example, Kepler cast numerous *horoscopes*—the predictive charts of astrology (Figure 3.28)—even as he was discovering the laws of planetary motion. However, given Kepler's later description of astrology as "the foolish stepdaughter of astronomy" and "a dreadful superstition," he may have cast the horoscopes solely as a source of much-needed income. Modern-day astrologers also claim Galileo as one of their own, in part for his having cast a horoscope for the Grand Duke of Tuscany. However, while Galileo's astronomical discoveries changed human history, the horoscope was just plain wrong: The Duke died just a few weeks after Galileo predicted that he would have a long and fruitful life.

The scientific triumph of Kepler and Galileo in showing Earth to be a planet orbiting the Sun heralded the end of the linkage between astronomy and astrology. Astronomy has since gained status as a successful science that helps us understand our universe, while astrology no longer has any connection to the modern science of astronomy.

Does astrology have any scientific validity?

Although astronomers gave up on it centuries ago, astrology remains popular with the general public. Many people read their daily horoscopes in newspapers, and some pay significant fees to have personal horoscopes cast by "professional" astrologers. Worldwide, more people earn incomes by casting horoscopes than through astronomical research, and books and articles on astrology often outsell all but the most popular books on astronomy. With so many people giving credence to astrology, is it possible that it has some scientific validity after all?

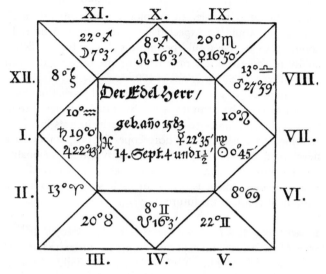

FIGURE 3.28 This chart, cast by Kepler, is an example of a horoscope.

Testing Astrology The validity of astrology can be difficult to assess, because there's no general agreement among astrologers even on such basic things as what astrology is or what it can predict. For example, "Western astrology" is quite different in nature from the astrology practiced in India and China. Some astrologers do not make testable predictions at all; rather, they give vague guidance about how to live one's life. Most newspaper horoscopes fall into this category. Although your horoscope may seem to ring true at first, a careful read will usually show it to be so vague as to be untestable. For example, a horoscope that says "It is a good day to spend time with your friends" may be good advice but doesn't offer much to test. If you read the horoscopes for all 12 astrological signs, you'll probably find that several of them apply equally well to you. When astrology offers only vague advice rather than testable predictions, the question of scientific validity does not apply.

> **SEE IT FOR YOURSELF**
> Look in a local newspaper for today's weather forecast and for your horoscope. Contrast the nature of their predictions. At the end of the day, you will know if the weather forecast was accurate. Can you also say whether the horoscope was accurate? Explain.

Nevertheless, most professional astrologers still earn their livings by casting horoscopes that either predict future events in an individual's life or describe characteristics of the person's personality and life. If the horoscope predicts future events, we can check to see whether the predictions come true. If it describes a person's personality and life, the description can be checked for accuracy. A scientific test of astrology requires evaluating many horoscopes and comparing their accuracies to what would be expected by pure chance. For example, suppose a horoscope states that a person's best friend is female. Because roughly half the population of the United States is female, an astrologer who casts 100 such horoscopes would be expected by pure chance to be right about 50 times. We would be impressed with the predictive ability of the astrologer only if he or she were right much more often than 50 times out of 100.

In hundreds of scientific tests, astrological predictions have never proved to be accurate by a substantially greater margin than expected from pure chance. Similarly, in tests in which astrologers are asked to cast horoscopes for people they have never met, the horoscopes fail to match actual personality profiles more often than expected by chance. The verdict is clear: The methods of astrology are useless for predicting the past, the present, or the future.

Examining the Underpinnings of Astrology In science, observations and experiments are the ultimate judge of any idea. No matter how outlandish an idea might appear, it cannot be dismissed if it successfully meets observational or experimental tests. The idea that Earth rotates and orbits the Sun at one time seemed outlandish, yet today it is so strongly supported by the evidence that we consider it a fact. The idea that the positions of the Sun, Moon, and planets among the stars influence our lives might sound outlandish today, but if astrology were to make predictions that came true, adherence to the principles of science would force us to take astrology seriously. However, given that scientific tests of astrology have never found any evidence that its predictive methods work, it is worth looking at its premises to see whether they make sense. Might there be a few kernels of wisdom buried within the lore of astrology?

Let's begin with one of the key premises of astrology: that there is special meaning in the patterns of the stars in the constellations. This idea may have seemed quite reasonable in ancient times, when the stars were assumed to be fixed on an unchanging celestial sphere, but today we know that the patterns of the stars in the constellations are accidents of the moment. Long ago the constellations did not look the same, and they will look still different far in the future [Section 1.3]. Moreover, the stars in a constellation don't necessarily have any *physical* association (see Figure 2.3). Because stars vary in distance, two stars that appear on opposite sides of our sky might be closer together than two stars in the same constellation. Constellations are only *apparent* associations of stars, with no more physical reality than the water in a desert mirage.

Astrology also places great importance on the positions of the planets among the constellations. Again, this idea might have seemed quite reasonable in ancient times, when it was thought that the planets truly wandered among the stars. Today we know that the planets only *appear* to wander among the stars. In reality, the planets are in our own solar system, while the stars are vastly farther away. It is difficult to see how mere appearances could have profound effects on our lives.

Many other ideas at the heart of astrology are equally suspect. For example, most astrologers claim that a proper horoscope must account for the positions of *all* the planets. Does that mean that all horoscopes cast before the discovery of Neptune in 1846 were invalid? If so, why didn't astrologers notice that something was wrong with their horoscopes and predict the existence of Neptune? (In contrast, astronomers *did* predict its existence; see the Special Topic box on p. 322.) Most astrologers have also included Pluto since its discovery in 1930; does that mean they should now stop including it since it has been demoted to "dwarf planet," or that they need to include Eris and other dwarf planets that may not yet have been discovered? And why stop with our own solar system; shouldn't horoscopes also depend on the positions of all planets orbiting all other stars? Given seemingly unanswerable questions like these, there seems little hope that astrology will ever meet its ancient goal of forecasting human events.

THE BIG PICTURE

• Putting Chapter 3 into Context

In this chapter, we focused on the scientific principles through which we have learned so much about the universe. Key "big picture" concepts from this chapter include the following:

- The basic ingredients of scientific thinking—careful observation and trial-and-error testing—are a part of everyone's experience. Modern science simply provides a way of organizing this thinking to facilitate the learning and sharing of new knowledge.

- Although our understanding of the universe is growing rapidly today, each new piece of knowledge builds on ideas that came before.

- The Copernican revolution, which overthrew the ancient Greek belief in an Earth-centered universe, did not occur instantaneously. It unfolded over a period of more than a century, during which many of the characteristics of modern science first appeared.

- Science exhibits several key features that distinguish it from nonscience and that in principle allow anyone to come to the same conclusions when studying a scientific question.

- Astronomy and astrology once developed hand in hand, but today they represent very different things.

3.1 THE ANCIENT ROOTS OF SCIENCE

- **In what ways do all humans use scientific thinking?** Scientific thinking relies on the same type of trial-and-error thinking that we use in our everyday lives, but in a carefully organized way.

- **How did astronomical observations benefit ancient societies?**  Ancient cultures used astronomical observations to help them keep track of time and the seasons, crucial skills for people who depended on agriculture for survival.

- **What did ancient civilizations achieve in astronomy?** Ancient astronomers were accomplished observers who learned to tell the time of day and the time of year, to track cycles of the Moon, and to observe planets and stars. Many ancient structures aided astronomical observations.

3.2 ANCIENT GREEK SCIENCE

- **Why does modern science trace its roots to the Greeks?** The Greeks developed **models** of nature and emphasized the importance of having the predictions of those models agree with observations of nature.

- **How did the Greeks explain planetary motion?** 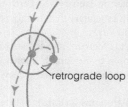 The Greek **geocentric model** reached its culmination with the **Ptolemaic model**, which explained apparent retrograde motion by having each planet move on a small circle whose center moves around Earth on a larger circle.

- **How was Greek knowledge preserved through history?** While Europe was in its Dark Ages, Islamic scholars preserved and extended ancient Greek knowledge. After the fall of Constantinople, scholars moved west to Europe, where their knowledge helped ignite the Renaissance.

3.3 THE COPERNICAN REVOLUTION

- **How did Copernicus, Tycho, and Kepler challenge the Earth-centered model?** Copernicus created a Sun-centered model of the solar system designed to replace the Ptolemaic model, but it was no more accurate than Ptolemy's because Copernicus still used perfect circles. Tycho's accurate, naked-eye observations provided the data needed to improve on Copernicus's model. Kepler developed a model of planetary motion that fit Tycho's data.

- **What are Kepler's three laws of planetary motion?**  (1) The orbit of each planet is an ellipse with the Sun at one focus. (2) As a planet moves around its orbit, it sweeps out equal areas in equal times. (3) More distant planets orbit the Sun at slower average speeds, obeying the mathematical relationship $p^2 = a^3$.

- **How did Galileo solidify the Copernican revolution?** 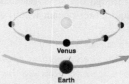 Galileo's experiments and telescopic observations overcame remaining objections to the Copernican idea of Earth as a planet orbiting the Sun. Although not everyone accepted his results immediately, in hindsight we see that Galileo sealed the case for the Sun-centered solar system.

3.4 THE NATURE OF SCIENCE

- **How can we distinguish science from nonscience?** Science generally exhibits three hallmarks: (1) Modern science seeks explanations for observed phenomena that rely solely on natural causes. (2) Science progresses through the creation and testing of models of nature that explain the observations as simply as possible. (3) A scientific model must make testable predictions about natural phenomena that would force us to revise or abandon the model if the predictions did not agree with observations.

- **What is a scientific theory?** A scientific **theory** is a simple yet powerful model that explains a wide variety of observations using just a few general principles and has been verified by repeated and varied testing.

3.5 ASTROLOGY

- **How is astrology different from astronomy?** Astronomy is a modern science that has taught us much about the universe. Astrology is a search for hidden influences on human lives based on the apparent positions of planets and stars in the sky; it does not follow the tenets of science.

- **Does astrology have any scientific validity?** Scientific tests have shown that astrological predictions do not prove to be accurate more than we can expect by pure chance, showing that the predictions have no scientific validity.

REVIEW QUESTIONS

Short-Answer Questions Based on the Reading

1. In what way is scientific thinking natural to all of us? How does modern science differ from this everyday type of thinking?

2. Why did ancient peoples study astronomy? Describe astronomical achievements of at least three ancient cultures.

3. How are the names of the 7 days of the week related to astronomical objects?

4. Describe at least three ways ancient peoples determined either the time of day or the time of year.

5. What is a lunar calendar? What is the Metonic cycle? Explain why the dates of Ramadan cycle through our solar calendar while the dates of Jewish holidays and Easter remain within about a 1 month period.

6. What do we mean by a *model* in science?

7. Summarize the development of the Greek *geocentric model*.

8. What do we mean by the *Ptolemaic model*? How did this model account for the apparent retrograde motion of planets in our sky?

9. What was the *Copernican revolution,* and how did it change the human view of the universe?

10. Why wasn't the Copernican model immediately accepted? Describe the roles of Tycho, Kepler, and Galileo in the eventual triumph of the Sun-centered model.

11. What is an *ellipse*? Define the *focus* and the *eccentricity* of an ellipse. Why are ellipses important in astronomy?

12. State each of *Kepler's laws of planetary motion*. Describe the meaning of each law in a way that almost anyone could understand.

13. Describe the three hallmarks of science and give an example of how we can see them in the unfolding of the Copernican revolution. What is *Occam's razor*? Why doesn't science accept personal testimony as evidence?

14. What is the difference between a *hypothesis* and a *theory* in science?

15. What do we mean by *pseudoscience*? How is it different from other types of nonscience?

16. What is the basic idea behind *astrology*? Explain why this idea seemed reasonable in ancient times but is no longer accepted by scientists.

TEST YOUR UNDERSTANDING

Science or Nonscience?

Each of the following statements makes some type of claim. Decide in each case whether the claim could be evaluated scientifically or whether it falls into the realm of nonscience. Explain clearly; not all of these have definitive answers, so your explanation is more important than your chosen answer.

17. The Yankees are the best baseball team of all time.

18. Several kilometers below its surface, Jupiter's moon Europa has an ocean of liquid water.

19. My house is haunted by ghosts who make the creaking noises I hear each night.

20. There is no liquid water on the surface of Mars today.

21. Dogs are smarter than cats.

22. Children born when Jupiter is in the constellation Taurus are more likely to be musicians than other children.

23. Aliens can manipulate time and memory so that they can abduct and perform experiments on people who never realize they were taken.

24. Newton's law of gravity works as well for explaining orbits of planets around other stars as it does for explaining orbits of the planets in our own solar system.

25. God created the laws of motion that were discovered by Newton.

26. A huge fleet of alien spacecraft will land on Earth and introduce an era of peace and prosperity on January 1, 2020.

Quick Quiz

Choose the best answer to each of the following. Explain your reasoning with one or more complete sentences.

27. In the Greek geocentric model, the retrograde motion of a planet occurs when (a) Earth is about to pass the planet in its orbit around the Sun. (b) the planet actually goes backward in its orbit around Earth. (c) the planet is aligned with the Moon in our sky.

28. Which of the following was *not* a major advantage of Copernicus's Sun-centered model over the Ptolemaic model? (a) It made significantly better predictions of planetary positions in our sky. (b) It offered a more natural explanation for the apparent retrograde motion of planets in our sky. (c) It allowed calculation of the orbital periods and distances of the planets.

29. When we say that a planet has a highly eccentric orbit, we mean that (a) it is spiraling in toward the Sun. (b) its orbit is an ellipse with the Sun at one focus. (c) in some parts of its orbit it is much closer to the Sun than in other parts.

30. Earth is closer to the Sun in January than in July. Therefore, in accord with Kepler's second law, (a) Earth travels faster in its orbit around the Sun in July than in January. (b) Earth travels faster in its orbit around the Sun in January than in July. (c) it is summer in January and winter in July.

31. According to Kepler's third law, (a) Mercury travels fastest in the part of its orbit in which it is closest to the Sun. (b) Jupiter orbits the Sun at a faster speed than Saturn. (c) all the planets have nearly circular orbits.

32. Tycho Brahe's contribution to astronomy included (a) inventing the telescope. (b) proving that Earth orbits the Sun. (c) collecting data that enabled Kepler to discover the laws of planetary motion.

33. Galileo's contribution to astronomy included (a) discovering the laws of planetary motion. (b) discovering the law of gravity. (c) making observations and conducting experiments that dispelled scientific objections to the Sun-centered model.

34. Which of the following is not true about scientific progress? (a) Science progresses through the creation and testing of models of nature. (b) Science advances only through the scientific method. (c) Science avoids explanations that invoke the supernatural.

35. Which of the following is *not* true about a scientific theory? (a) A theory must explain a wide range of observations or experiments. (b) Even the strongest theories can never be proved true beyond all doubt. (c) A theory is essentially an educated guess.

36. When Einstein's theory of gravity (general relativity) gained acceptance, it demonstrated that Newton's theory had been (a) wrong. (b) incomplete. (c) really only a guess.

PROCESS OF SCIENCE

Examining How Science Works

37. *What Makes It Science?* Choose a single idea in the modern view of the cosmos as discussed in Chapter 1, such as "The universe is expanding," "The universe began with a Big Bang," "We are made

from elements manufactured by stars," or "The Sun orbits the center of the Milky Way Galaxy once every 230 million years."

a. Describe how the idea you have chosen is rooted in each of the three hallmarks of science discussed in this chapter; that is, explain how it is based on observations, how our understanding of it depends on a model, and how the model is testable.   b. Describe a hypothetical observation that, if it were actually made, might cause us to call the idea into question. Then briefly discuss whether you think that, overall, the idea is likely or unlikely to hold up to future observations.

38. *Earth's Shape*. It took thousands of years for humans to deduce that Earth is spherical. For each of the following alternative models of Earth's shape, identify one or more observations that you could make for yourself and that would invalidate the model.

a. A flat Earth   b. A cylindrical Earth, like that proposed by Anaximander   c. A football-shaped Earth

39. *Scientific Test of Astrology*. Find out about at least one scientific test of the validity of astrology. Write a short summary of the methods and results of the test.

40. *Your Own Astrological Test*. Devise your own scientific test of astrology. Clearly define your methods and how you will evaluate the results. Carry out the test and write a short report about it.

INVESTIGATE FURTHER

In-Depth Questions to Increase Your Understanding

Short-Answer/Essay Questions

41. *Lunar Calendars.*

a. Find the dates of the Jewish festival of Chanukah for this year and the next 3 years. Based on what you have learned in this chapter, explain why the dates change as they do.   b. Find the dates of the Muslim fast for Ramadan for this year and the next 3 years. Based on what you have learned in this chapter, explain why the dates change as they do.

42. *Copernican Players*. Using a bulleted list format, make a one-page "executive summary" of the major roles that Copernicus, Tycho, Kepler, and Galileo played in overturning the ancient belief in an Earth-centered universe.

43. *Influence on History*. Based on what you have learned about the Copernican revolution, write a one- to two-page essay about how you believe it altered the course of human history.

44. *Cultural Astronomy*. Choose a particular culture of interest to you, and research the astronomical knowledge and accomplishments of that culture. Write a two- to three-page summary of your findings.

45. *Astronomical Structures*. Choose an ancient astronomical structure of interest to you (e.g., Stonehenge, Templo Mayor, Pawnee lodges) and research its history. Write a two- to three-page summary of your findings. If possible, also build a scale model of the structure or create detailed diagrams to illustrate how the structure was used.

46. *Venus and the Mayans*. The planet Venus apparently played a particularly important role in Mayan society. Research the evidence and write a one- to two-page summary of current knowledge about the role of Venus in Mayan society.

Quantitative Problems

Be sure to show all calculations clearly and state your final answers in complete sentences.

47. *The Metonic Cycle*. The length of our calendar year is 365.2422 days, and the Moon's monthly cycle of phases averages 29.5306 days in length. By calculating the number of days in each, confirm that 19 solar years is almost precisely equal to 235 cycles of the lunar phases. Show your work clearly, then write a few sentences explaining how this fact can be used to keep a lunar calendar roughly synchronized with a solar calendar.

48. *Chinese Calendar*. The traditional Chinese lunar calendar has 12 months in most years but adds a thirteenth month to 22 of every 60 years. How many days does this give the Chinese calendar in each 60-year period? How does this compare to the number of days in 60 years on a solar calendar? Based on your answers, explain how this scheme is similar to the scheme used by lunar calendars that follow the Metonic cycle. (*Hint:* You'll need the data given in Problem 47.)

49. *Method of Eratosthenes I*. You are an astronomer on planet Nearth, which orbits a distant star. It has recently been accepted that Nearth is spherical in shape, though no one knows its size. One day, while studying in the library of Alectown, you learn that on the equinox your sun is directly overhead in the city of Nyene, located 1000 kilometers due north of you. On the equinox, you go outside and observe that the altitude of your sun is 80°. What is the circumference of Nearth? (*Hint:* Apply the technique used by Eratosthenes to measure Earth's circumference.)

50. *Method of Eratosthenes II*. You are an astronomer on planet Tirth, which orbits a distant star. It has recently been accepted that Tirth is spherical in shape, though no one knows its size. One day, you learn that on the equinox your sun is directly overhead in the city of Tyene, located 400 kilometers due north of you. On the equinox, you go outside and observe that the altitude of your sun is 86°. What is the circumference of Tirth? (*Hint:* Apply the technique used by Eratosthenes to measure Earth's circumference.)

51. *Mars Orbit*. Find the perihelion and aphelion distances of Mars. (*Hint:* You'll need data from Appendix E.)

52. *Most Eccentric Orbit*. Which planet in our solar system has the most eccentric orbit? Find the planet's perihelion and aphelion distances.

53. *Least Eccentric Orbit*. Which planet in our solar system has the least eccentric orbit? Find the planet's perihelion and aphelion distances.

54. *Eris Orbit*. The recently discovered Eris, which is slightly larger than Pluto, orbits the Sun every 560 years. What is its average distance (semimajor axis) from the Sun? How does its average distance compare to that of Pluto?

55. *New Planet Orbit*. A newly discovered planet orbits a distant star with the same mass as the Sun at an average distance of 112 million kilometers. Its orbital eccentricity is 0.3. Find the planet's orbital period and its nearest and farthest orbital distances from its star.

56. *Halley Orbit*. Halley's Comet orbits the Sun every 76.0 years and has an orbital eccentricity of 0.97.

a. Find its average distance from the Sun (semimajor axis).
b. Find its perihelion and aphelion distances. Does Halley's Comet spend most of its time near its perihelion distance, near its aphelion distance, or halfway in between? Explain.

Discussion Questions

57. *The Impact of Science*. The modern world is filled with ideas, knowledge, and technology that developed through science and application of the scientific method. Discuss some of these things and how they affect our lives. Which of these impacts do you think are positive? Which are negative? Overall, do you think science has benefited the human race? Defend your opinion.

58. *The Importance of Ancient Astronomy*. Why was astronomy important to people in ancient times? Discuss both the practical importance of astronomy and the importance it may have had for religious or other traditions. Which do you think was

more important in the development of ancient astronomy: its practical or its philosophical role? Defend your opinion.

59. *Astronomy and Astrology.* Why do you think astrology remains so popular around the world even though it has failed all scientific tests of its validity? Do you think the popularity of astrology has any positive or negative social consequences? Defend your opinions.

Web Projects

60. *Easter.* Research when different denominations of Christianity celebrate Easter and why they use different dates. Summarize your findings in a one- to two-page report.

61. *Greek Astronomers.* Many ancient Greek scientists had ideas that, in retrospect, seem well ahead of their time. Learn more about one of the following ancient Greek scientists, and write a one- to two-page "scientific biography" of your chosen person.

Thales   Meton   Archimedes
Anaxagoras   Aristotle   Hipparchus

Hypatia   Eratosthenes   Aristarchus
Anaximander   Seleucus   Apollonius
Empedocles   Pythagoras   Ptolemy
Plato   Democritus
Callipus   Eudoxus

62. *The Ptolemaic Model.* This chapter gives only a very brief description of Ptolemy's model of the universe. Investigate this model in greater depth. Using diagrams and text as needed, give a two- to three-page description of the model.

63. *The Galileo Affair.* In recent years, the Roman Catholic Church has devoted a lot of resources to learning more about the trial of Galileo and to understanding past actions of the Church in the Galilean case. Learn more about these studies and write a short report about the Vatican's current view of the case.

64. *Science or Pseudoscience.* Choose a pseudoscientific claim related to astronomy, and learn more about how scientists have "debunked" it. (A good starting point is the Bad Astronomy Web site.) Write a short summary of your findings.

VISUAL SKILLS CHECK

Use the following questions to check your understanding of some of the many types of visual information used in astronomy. Answers are provided in Appendix J. For additional practice, try the Chapter 3 Visual Quiz at www.masteringastronomy.com.

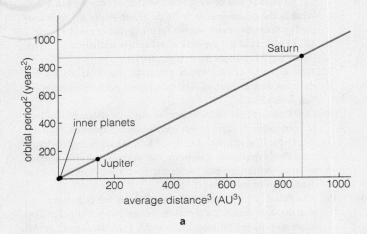

a

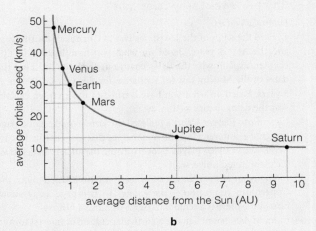

b

Study the two graphs above, based on Figure 3.21. Use the information in the graphs to answer the following questions.

1. Approximately how fast is Jupiter orbiting the Sun?
   a. cannot be determined from the information provided   b. 20 km/s   c. 10 km/s   d. a little less than 15 km/s
2. An asteroid with an average orbital distance of 2 AU will orbit the Sun at an average speed that is _____.
   a. a little slower than the orbital speed of Mars   b. a little faster than the orbital speed of Mars   c. the same as the orbital speed of Mars
3. Uranus, not shown on graph b, orbits about 19 AU from the Sun. Based on the graph, its approximate orbital speed is between about _____.
   a. 20 and 25 km/s   b. 15 and 20 km/s   c. 10 and 15 km/s   d. 5 and 10 km/s
4. Kepler's third law is often stated as $p^2 = a^3$. The value a^3 for a planet is shown on _____.
   a. the horizontal axis of graph a   b. the vertical axis of graph a   c. the horizontal axis of graph b   d. the vertical axis of graph b

5. On graph a, you can see Kepler's third law ($p^2 = a^3$) from the fact that _____ .
   a. the data fall on a straight line   b. the axes are labeled with values for p^2 and a^3 c. the planet names are labeled on the graph
6. Suppose graph a showed a planet on the red line directly above a value of 1000 AU^3 along the horizontal axis. On the vertical axis, this planet would be at _____ .
   a. 1000 years^2 b. 1000^2 years^2 c. $\sqrt{1000}$ years^2 d. 100 years
7. How far does the planet in question 6 orbit from the Sun?
   a. 10 AU   b. 100 AU   c. 1000 AU   d. $\sqrt{1000}$ AU

S1
CELESTIAL TIMEKEEPING AND NAVIGATION
SUPPLEMENTARY CHAPTER

LEARNING GOALS

S1.1 ASTRONOMICAL TIME PERIODS

- How do we define the day, month, year, and planetary periods?
- How do we tell the time of day?
- When and why do we have leap years?

S1.2 CELESTIAL COORDINATES AND MOTION IN THE SKY

- How do we locate objects on the celestial sphere?
- How do stars move through the local sky?
- How does the Sun move through the local sky?

S1.3 PRINCIPLES OF CELESTIAL NAVIGATION

- How can you determine your latitude?
- How can you determine your longitude?

Socrates: Shall we make astronomy the next study? What do you say?

Glaucon: Certainly. A working knowledge of the seasons, months, and years is beneficial to everyone, to commanders as well as to farmers and sailors.

Socrates: You make me smile, Glaucon. You are so afraid that the public will accuse you of recommending unprofitable studies.

—Plato, *Republic*

In ancient times, the practical needs for timekeeping and navigation were important reasons for the study of astronomy. The celestial origins of timekeeping and navigation are still evident. The time of day comes from the location of the Sun in the local sky, the month comes from the Moon's cycle of phases, and the year comes from the Sun's annual path along the ecliptic. The very name of the "North Star" tells us how it can be an aid to navigation.

We can now tell the time by glancing at an inexpensive electronic watch and navigate with handheld devices that receive signals from satellites of the global positioning system (GPS). But knowing the celestial basis of timekeeping and navigation can still be useful, particularly for understanding the rich history of astronomical discovery. In this chapter, we will explore the apparent motions of the Sun, Moon, and planets in greater detail, which will allow us to study the principles of celestial timekeeping and navigation.

S1.1 ASTRONOMICAL TIME PERIODS

Today, our clocks and calendars are beautifully synchronized to the rhythms of the heavens. Precision measurements allow us to ensure that our clocks keep pace with the Sun's daily trek across our sky, while our calendar holds the dates of the equinoxes and solstices as steady as possible. In earlier chapters, we saw how this synchronicity took root in ancient observations of the sky. However, it is only much more recently that we have come to understand the details of timekeeping. In this section, we will look more closely at basic measures of time and our modern, international system of timekeeping.

How do we define the day, month, year, and planetary periods?

By now you know that the length of the day corresponds to Earth's rotation, the length of the month to the cycle of lunar phases, and the length of the year to our orbit around the Sun. However, when we look carefully at each case, we find that the correspondence is not quite as simple as we might at first guess. Instead, we are forced to define two different types of day, month, and year. We also define planetary periods in two different ways. Let's take a look at how and why we make these distinctions.

The Length of the Day We usually think of a day as the time it takes for Earth to rotate once, but if you measure this time period you'll find that it is *not* exactly 24 hours. Instead, Earth's rotation period is about 4 minutes short of 24 hours. What's going on?

We can understand the answer by thinking about the movement of the stars and Sun across our sky. Remember that the daily circling of the stars in our sky is an illusion created by Earth's rotation (see Figure 2.9). You can therefore measure Earth's rotation period by measuring how long it takes for any star to go from its highest point in the sky one day to its highest point the next day (Figure S1.1a). This time period, which we call a **sidereal day**, is about 23 hours 56 minutes (more precisely, $23^h 56^m 4.09^s$). *Sidereal* (pronounced *sy-DEAR-ee-al*) means "related to the stars"; note that you'll measure the same time no matter what star you choose. For practical purposes, the sidereal day is Earth's precise rotation period.

Our 24-hour day, which we call a **solar day**, is based on the time it takes for the *Sun* to make one circuit around the local sky. You can measure this time period by measuring how long

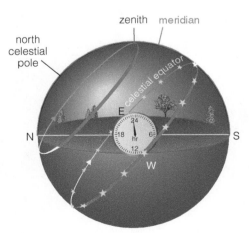

a A sidereal day is the time it takes any star to make a circuit of the local sky. It is about 23 hours 56 minutes.

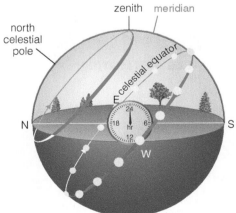

FIGURE S1.1 Using the sky to measure the length of a day.

b A solar day is measured similarly, but by timing the Sun rather than a distant star. The length of the solar day varies over the course of the year but averages 24 hours.

it takes the Sun to go from its highest point in the sky one day to its highest point the next day (Figure S1.1b). The solar day is indeed 24 hours on average, although it varies slightly (up to 25 seconds longer or shorter than 24 hours) over the course of a year.

A simple demonstration shows why the solar day is about 4 minutes longer than the sidereal day. Set an object to represent the Sun on a table, and stand a few steps away to represent Earth. Point at the Sun and imagine that you also happen to be pointing toward a distant star that lies in the same direction. If you rotate (counterclockwise) while standing in place, you'll again be pointing at both the Sun and the star after one full rotation (Figure S1.2a). However, because Earth rotates at the same time it orbits the Sun, you can make the demonstration more realistic by taking a couple of steps around the Sun (counterclockwise) while you rotate (Figure S1.2b). After one full rotation, you will again be pointing in the direction of the distant star, so this represents a sidereal day. But it does not represent a solar day, because you will not yet be pointing back at the Sun. If you wish to point again at the Sun, you need to make up for your orbital motion by making slightly more than one full rotation. This "extra" bit of rotation makes a solar day longer than a sidereal day.

The only problem with this demonstration is that it exaggerates Earth's daily orbital motion. Because Earth takes about 365 days (1 year) to make a full 360° orbit around the Sun, Earth actually moves only about 1° per day around its orbit. Thus, a solar day represents about 361° of rotation, rather than the 360° for a sidereal day (Figure S1.2c). The extra 1° rotation takes about $\frac{1}{360}$ of Earth's rotation period, which is about 4 minutes.

The Length of the Month As we discussed in Chapter 2, our month comes from the Moon's $29\frac{1}{2}$-day cycle of phases (think "moonth"). More technically, the $29\frac{1}{2}$-day period required for each cycle of phases is called a **synodic month**. The word *synodic* comes from the Latin *synod*, which means "meeting." A synodic month gets its name because the Sun and the Moon "meet" in the sky with every new moon.

Just as a solar day is not Earth's true rotation period, a synodic month is not the Moon's true orbital period. Earth's motion around the Sun means that the Moon must complete more than one full orbit of Earth from one new moon to the next (Figure S1.3). The Moon's true orbital period, or **sidereal month**, is only about $27\frac{1}{3}$ days. Like the sidereal day, the sidereal month gets its name because it describes how long it takes the Moon to complete an orbit relative to the positions of distant stars.

The Length of the Year A year is related to Earth's orbital period, but again there are two slightly different definitions. The time it takes for Earth to complete one orbit relative to the stars is called a **sidereal year**. But our calendar is based on the cycle of the seasons, which we measure as the time from the spring equinox one year to the spring equinox the next year. This time period, called a **tropical year**, is about 20 minutes shorter than the sidereal year. A 20-minute difference might not seem like much, but it would make a calendar based on the sidereal year get out of sync with the seasons by 1 day every 72 years—a difference that would add up over centuries.

The difference between the sidereal year and the tropical year arises from Earth's 26,000-year cycle of axis precession [Section 2.2]. Precession not only changes the orientation of the axis in space but also changes the locations in Earth's orbit at which the seasons occur. Each year, the location of the equinoxes and solstices among the stars shifts about $\frac{1}{26,000}$ of the way around the orbit. If you do the math, you'll find that $\frac{1}{26,000}$ of a year is about 20 minutes, which explains the 20-minute difference between the tropical year and the sidereal year.

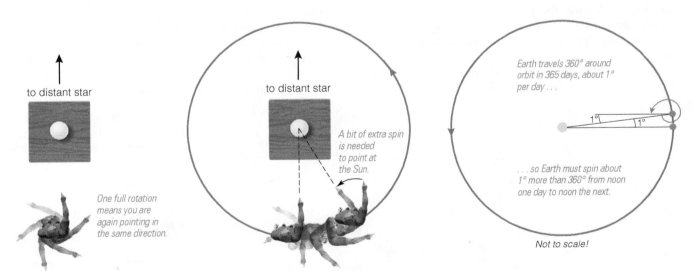

a One full rotation represents a sidereal day and means that you are again pointing to the same distant star.

b While you are "orbiting" the Sun, one rotation still returns you to pointing at a distant star, but you need slightly more than one full rotation to return to pointing at the Sun.

c Earth travels about 1° per day around its orbit, so a solar day requires about 361° of rotation.

to distant star

One full rotation means you are again pointing in the same direction.

to distant star

A bit of extra spin is needed to point at the Sun.

Earth travels 360° around orbit in 365 days, about 1° per day . . .

1°   1°

. . . so Earth must spin about 1° more than 360° from noon one day to noon the next.

Not to scale!

FIGURE S1.2 A demonstration showing why a solar day is slightly longer than a sidereal day.

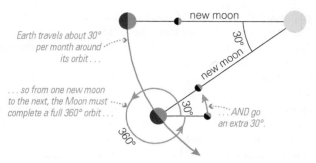

new moon

Earth travels about 30° per month around its orbit . . .

. . . so from one new moon to the next, the Moon must complete a full 360° orbit . . .

360°

new moon

30°

30°

30°

. . . AND go an extra 30°.

FIGURE S1.3 Interactive Figure The Moon completes one 360° orbit in about $27\frac{1}{3}$ days (a sidereal month), but the time from new moon to new moon is about $29\frac{1}{2}$ days (a synodic month).

Planetary Periods Although planetary periods are not used in our modern timekeeping, they were important to many ancient cultures. For example, the Mayan calendar was based in part on the apparent motions of Venus. In addition, Copernicus's ability to determine orbital periods of planets with his Sun-centered model played an important role in keeping the model alive long enough for its ultimate acceptance [Section 3.3].

A planet's **sidereal period** is the time the planet takes to orbit the Sun. (As usual, it has the name *sidereal* because it is measured relative to distant stars.) For example, Jupiter's sidereal period is 11.86 years, so it takes about 12 years for Jupiter to make a complete circuit through the constellations of the zodiac. Jupiter therefore appears to move through roughly one zodiac constellation each year. If Jupiter is currently in Pisces (as it is for much of 2010 and 2011), it will be in Aries at this time next year and Taurus the following year, returning to Pisces in about 12 years.

A planet's **synodic period** is the time between when it is lined up with the Sun in our sky at one time and the next similar alignment. (As with the Moon, the term *synodic* refers to the planet's "meeting" the Sun in the sky.) Figure S1.4 shows that the situation is somewhat different for planets nearer the Sun than Earth (that is, Mercury and Venus) than for planets farther away.

Look first at the situation for the more distant planet in Figure S1.4. As seen from Earth, this planet will sometimes

line up with the Sun in what we call a **conjunction**. At other times, it will appear exactly opposite the Sun in our sky, or at **opposition**. We cannot see the planet during conjunction with the Sun because it is hidden by the Sun's glare and rises and sets with the Sun in our sky. At opposition, the planet moves through the sky like the full moon, rising at sunset, reaching the meridian at midnight, and setting at dawn. Note that the planet is closest to Earth at opposition and hence appears brightest in our sky at this time.

Now look at the planet that is *nearer* than Earth to the Sun in Figure S1.4. This planet never has an opposition but instead has two conjunctions—an "inferior conjunction" between Earth and the Sun and a "superior conjunction" when the planet appears behind the Sun as seen from Earth. Two other points are important for the inner planets: their points of **greatest elongation**, when they appear farthest from the Sun in our sky. At its greatest eastern elongation, Venus appears about 46° east of the Sun in our sky, which means it shines brightly in the evening. Similarly, at its greatest western elongation, Venus appears about 46° west of the Sun and shines brightly before dawn. In between the times when Venus appears in the morning sky and the times when it appears in the evening sky, Venus disappears from view for a few weeks with each conjunction. Mercury's pattern is similar, but because it is closer to the Sun, it never appears more than about 28° from the Sun in our sky. That makes Mercury difficult to see, because it is almost always obscured by the glare of the Sun.

THINK ABOUT IT

Do we ever see Mercury or Venus at midnight? Explain.

As you study Figure S1.4, you might wonder whether Mercury or Venus ever falls directly in front of the Sun at inferior conjunction, creating a mini-eclipse as it blocks a little of the Sun's light. They do, but only rarely, because their orbital planes are slightly tilted compared to Earth's orbital plane (the ecliptic plane). As a result, Mercury and Venus usually appear slightly above or below the Sun at inferior conjunction. But on rare occasions, we do indeed see Mercury or Venus appear to pass directly across the face of the Sun during inferior conjunction (Figure S1.5). Such

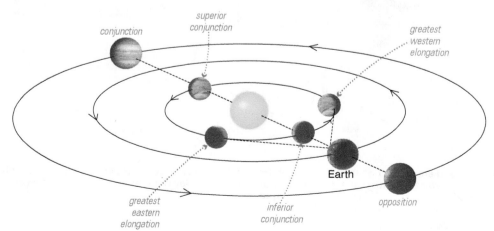

conjunction

superior conjunction

greatest western elongation

greatest eastern elongation

inferior conjunction

opposition

Earth

FIGURE S1.4 This diagram shows important positions of planets relative to Earth and the Sun. For a planet farther from the Sun than Earth (such as Jupiter), conjunction occurs when the planet appears aligned with the Sun in the sky, and opposition occurs when the planet appears on our meridian at midnight. Planets nearer the Sun (such as Venus) have two conjunctions and never get farther from the Sun in our sky than at their greatest elongations. (Adapted from *Advanced Skywatching,* by Burnham et al.)

FIGURE S1.5 This photo was taken in Florida during the transit of Venus on June 8, 2004. Venus is the small black dot near the right edge of the Sun's face.

events are called **transits**. Mercury transits occur an average of a dozen times per century; the first one in this century occurred on November 8, 2006, and the next will occur on May 9, 2016. Venus transits come in pairs 8 years apart, with more than a century between the second of one pair and the first of the next. We are currently between the two transits of a pair: The first occurred on June 8, 2004, and the second will occur on June 6, 2012. After that, it will be 105 years until the first of the next pair of Venus transits, which will occur in 2117 and 2125.

How do we tell the time of day?

Telling time seems simple, but in fact there are several different ways to define the time of day, even after we agree that time should be based on the 24-hour solar day. Let's explore some of the ways of telling time and see how they ultimately led to our modern system in which we can synchronize clocks anywhere in the world.

Apparent Solar Time If we base time on the Sun's *actual* position in the local sky, as is the case when we use a sundial (Figure S1.6), we are measuring **apparent solar time**. Noon is the precise moment when the Sun is highest in the sky (on the meridian) and the sundial casts its shortest shadow. Before noon, when the Sun is rising upward through the sky, the apparent solar time is *ante meridiem* ("before the middle of the day"), or a.m. For example, if the Sun will reach the meridian 2 hours from now, the apparent solar time is 10 a.m. After noon, the apparent solar time is *post meridiem* ("after the middle of the day"), or p.m. If the Sun crossed the meridian 3 hours ago, the apparent solar time is 3 p.m. Note that, technically, noon and midnight are *neither* a.m. nor p.m. However, by convention we usually say that noon is 12 p.m. and midnight is 12 a.m.

THINK ABOUT IT

Is it daytime or nighttime at 12:01 a.m.? 12:01 p.m.? Explain.

Mean Solar Time Suppose you set a clock to precisely 12:00 when a sundial shows noon today. If every solar day were precisely 24 hours, your clock would always remain synchronized with the sundial. However, while 24 hours is the *average* length of the solar day, the actual length of the solar

FIGURE S1.6 A basic sundial consists of a dial marked by numerals, and a stick, or *gnomon*, that casts a shadow. Here, the shadow is on the Roman numeral I, indicating that the apparent solar time is 1:00 p.m. (The portion of the dial without numerals represents nighttime hours.) Because the Sun's path across the local sky depends on latitude, a particular sundial will be accurate only for a particular latitude.

day varies throughout the year. As a result, your clock will not remain perfectly synchronized with the sundial. For example, your clock is likely to read a few seconds before or after 12:00 when the sundial reads noon tomorrow, and within a few weeks your clock time may differ from the apparent solar time by several minutes. Your clock (assuming it is accurate) will again be synchronized with the Sun on the same date next year, since it keeps track of the average length of the solar day.

If we average the differences between the time a clock would read and the time a sundial would read, we can define **mean solar time** (*mean* is another word for *average*). A clock set to mean solar time reads 12:00 each day at the time that the Sun crosses the meridian *on average*. The actual mean solar time at which the Sun crosses the meridian varies over the course of the year in a fairly complex way (see "Solar Days and the Analemma," p. 95). The result is that, on any given day, a clock set to mean solar time may read anywhere

from about 17 minutes before noon to 15 minutes after noon (that is, from 11:43 a.m. to 12:15 p.m.) when a sundial indicates noon.

Although the lack of perfect synchronization with the Sun might at first sound like a drawback, mean solar time is actually more convenient than apparent solar time (the sundial time)— as long as you have access to a mechanical or electronic clock. Once set, a reliable mechanical or electronic clock can always tell you the mean solar time. In contrast, precisely measuring apparent solar time requires a sundial, which is useless at night or when it is cloudy.

Like apparent solar time, mean solar time is a *local* measure of time. That is, it varies with longitude because of Earth's west-to-east rotation. For example, clocks in New York are set 3 hours ahead of clocks in Los Angeles. If clocks were set precisely to local mean solar time, they would vary even over relatively short east-west distances. For example,

The Copernican Layout of the Solar System

As discussed in Chapter 3, Copernicus favored the Sun-centered model partly because it allowed him to calculate orbital periods and distances for the planets. Let's see how the Copernican system allows us to determine orbital (sidereal) periods of the planets.

We cannot directly measure orbital periods, because our own movement around the Sun means that we look at the planets from different points in our orbit at different times. However, we can measure synodic periods simply by seeing how much time passes between one particular alignment (such as opposition or inferior conjunction) and the next. Figure 1 shows the geometry for a planet *farther from the Sun than Earth* (such as Jupiter), under the assumption of circular orbits (which is what Copernicus assumed). Study the figure carefully to notice the following key facts:

- The dashed brown curve shows the planet's complete orbit. The time the planet requires for one complete orbit is its orbital (sidereal) period, P_{orb}.

- The solid brown arrow shows how far the planet travels along its orbit from one opposition to the next. The time between oppositions is defined as its synodic period, P_{syn}.

- The dashed blue curve shows Earth's complete orbit; Earth takes $P_{Earth} = 1$ yr to complete an orbit.

- The solid red curve (and red arrow) shows how far Earth goes during the planet's synodic period; it is *more* than one complete orbit because Earth must travel a little "extra" to catch back up with the other planet. The time it takes Earth to travel the "extra" distance (the thick part of the red curve) must be the planet's synodic period minus 1 year, or $P_{syn} - 1$ yr.

- The angle that the planet sweeps out during its synodic period is equal to the angle that Earth sweeps out as it travels the "extra" distance. Thus, the *ratio* of the planet's complete orbital period (P_{orb}) to its synodic period (P_{syn}) must be equal to the *ratio* of Earth's orbital period (1 yr) to the time required for the "extra" distance (see Appendix C.5 for a review of ratios). Since we already found that the time required for this extra distance is $P_{syn} - 1$ yr, we write:

$$\frac{P_{orb}}{P_{syn}} = \frac{1 \text{ yr}}{(P_{syn} - 1 \text{ yr})}$$

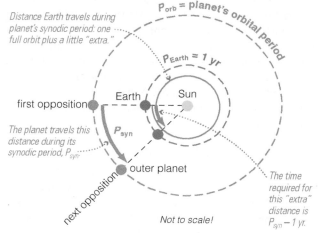

Distance Earth travels during planet's synodic period: one full orbit plus a little "extra."

P_{orb} = planet's orbital period

$P_{Earth} = 1$ yr

Sun

Earth

first opposition

The planet travels this distance during its synodic period, P_{syn}.

P_{syn}

next opposition

outer planet

The time required for this "extra" distance is $P_{syn} - 1$ yr.

Not to scale!

FIGURE 1

Multiplying both sides by P_{syn} gives us the final equation:

$$P_{orb} = P_{syn} \times \frac{1 \text{ yr}}{(P_{syn} - 1 \text{ yr})}$$

[for planets farther from the Sun than Earth]

The geometry is slightly different when Earth is the outer planet, as shown in Figure 2. In this case the two equal ratios are $1 \text{ yr}/P_{syn} = P_{orb}/(P_{syn} - P_{orb})$. With a little algebra, you can solve this equation for P_{orb}:

$$P_{orb} = P_{syn} \times \frac{1 \text{ yr}}{(P_{syn} + 1 \text{ yr})}$$

[for planets closer to the Sun than Earth]

Copernicus knew the synodic periods of the planets and was therefore able to use the above equations (in a slightly different form) to calculate their true orbital periods. He was then able to use the geometry of planetary alignments to compute the distances to the planets in terms of the Earth-Sun distance. (That is, he calculated distances in AU, but he did not have a method for determining how far Earth is from the Sun.) His results, which were quite close to modern values, made so mean solar clocks in central Los Angeles would be about 2 minutes behind mean solar clocks in Pasadena, because Pasadena is slightly to the east.

Standard, Daylight, and Universal Time Clocks displaying mean solar time were common during the early history of the United States. However, by the late 1800s, the growth of railroad travel made the use of mean solar time increasingly problematic. Some states had dozens of different "official" times, usually corresponding to mean solar time in dozens of different cities, and each railroad company made schedules according to its own "railroad time." The many time systems made it difficult for passengers to follow the scheduling of trains.

On November 18, 1883, the railroad companies agreed to a new system that divided the United States into four time zones, setting all clocks within each zone to the same time. That was the birth of **standard time**, which today divides the entire world into time zones (Figure S1.7). Depending on where you live within a time zone, your standard time may vary somewhat from your mean solar time. In principle, the standard time in a particular time zone is the mean solar time in the *center* of the time zone, so that local mean solar time within a 1-hour-wide time zone would never differ by more than a half-hour from standard time. However, time zones often have unusual shapes to conform to social, economic, and political realities, so larger variations between standard time and mean solar time sometimes occur.

In most parts of the United States, clocks are set to standard time for only part of the year. Between the second Sunday in March and the first Sunday in November,* most of the United States changes to **daylight saving time**, which is 1 hour ahead of standard time. Because of the 1-hour advance with daylight saving time, clocks read around 1 p.m. (rather than around noon) when the Sun is on the meridian.

---

*These dates for daylight saving time took effect in 2007; before that, daylight saving time ran between the first Sunday in April and the last Sunday in October.

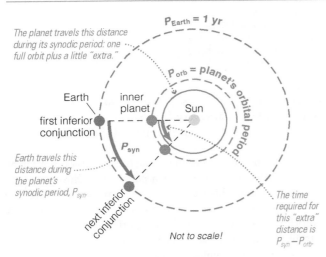

The planet travels this distance during its synodic period: one full orbit plus a little "extra."

$P_{Earth} = 1\ yr$

$P_{orb} = $ planet's orbital period

Earth

inner planet

Sun

first inferior conjunction

P_{syn}

Earth travels this distance during the planet's synodic period, P_{syn}.

next inferior conjunction

Not to scale!

The time required for this "extra" distance is $P_{syn} - P_{orb}$.

FIGURE 2

much sense to him that he felt he must have uncovered some deep truth about nature.

EXAMPLE 1: Jupiter's synodic period is 398.9 days, or 1.092 years. What is its actual orbital period?

SOLUTION:

Step 1 Understand: We are given Jupiter's synodic period (P_{syn} in the above equations) and are asked to find its orbital period (P_{orb}). Because Jupiter is farther from the Sun than Earth, we can use the first equation.

Step 2 Solve: We use the equation for a planet farther from the Sun than Earth with $P_{syn} = 1.092$ yr (Jupiter's synodic period):

$$P_{orb} = P_{syn} \times \frac{1\ yr}{(P_{syn} - 1\ yr)}$$

$$= 1.092\ yr \times \frac{1\ yr}{(1.092\ yr - 1\ yr)}$$

$$= 11.87\ yr$$

Step 3 Explain: We have found that Jupiter's orbital period is 11.87 years. In other words, simply by measuring the time that passes from when Jupiter is opposite the Sun in one year to when it is again opposite the next year (which is Jupiter's synodic period), we have learned that Jupiter takes a little less than 12 years to orbit the Sun. Notice that the answer makes sense in that it is longer than Earth's orbital period of 1 year, just as we expect for a planet that is farther than Earth from the Sun.

EXAMPLE 2: Venus's synodic period is 583.9 days. What is its actual orbital period?

SOLUTION:

Step 1 Understand: We are given Venus's synodic period, $P_{syn} = 583.9$ days, and are asked to find its orbital period. Because Venus is closer to the Sun than Earth, we need the second equation. Also, because we are given Venus's synodic period in days, for unit consistency we need to convert it to years; you should confirm that 583.9 days = 1.599 yr.

Step 2 Solve: We simply plug the value of P_{syn} into the equation for a planet closer to the Sun than Earth:

$$P_{orb} = P_{syn} \times \frac{1\ yr}{(P_{syn} + 1\ yr)}$$

$$= 1.599\ yr \times \frac{1\ yr}{(1.599\ yr + 1\ yr)}$$

$$= 0.6152\ yr$$

Step 3 Explain: We have found that Venus takes 0.6152 year to orbit the Sun. This number is easier to interpret if we convert it to days or months; you should confirm that it is equivalent to 224.7 days, or about $7\frac{1}{2}$ months. Notice that the answer makes sense in that it is shorter than Earth's orbital period of 1 year, just as we expect for a planet that is closer than Earth to the Sun.

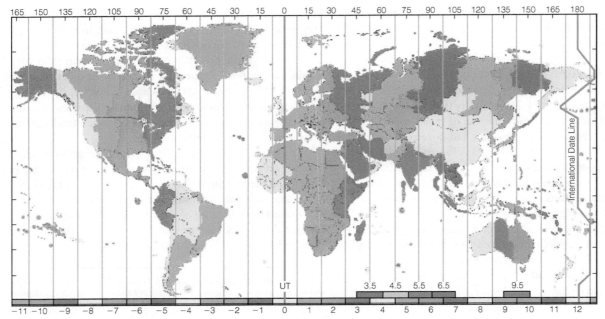

FIGURE S1.7 Time zones around the world. The numerical scale at the bottom shows hours ahead of (positive numbers) or behind (negative numbers) the time in Greenwich, England; the scale at the top is longitude. The vertical lines show standard time zones as they would be in the absence of political considerations. The color-coded regions show the actual time zones. Note, for example, that all of China uses the same standard time, even though the country is wide enough to span several time zones. Note also that a few countries use time zones centered on a half-hour (the upper set of colored bars), rather than an hour, relative to Greenwich time.

For purposes of navigation and astronomy, it is useful to have a single time for the entire Earth. For historical reasons, this "world" time was chosen to be the mean solar time in Greenwich, England—the place that also defines longitude 0° (see Figure 2.11). Today, this *Greenwich mean time (GMT)* is often called **universal time (UT)**. (Outside astronomy, it is more commonly called *universal coordinated time* [UTC]. Many airlines and weather services call it "Zulu time," because Greenwich's time zone is designated "Z" and "zulu" is a common way of phonetically identifying the letter *Z*.)

MA Seasons Tutorial, Lesson 2

When and why do we have leap years?

Our modern calendar is based on the length of the tropical year, which is the amount of time from one spring equinox to the next. The calendar is therefore designed to stay synchronized with the seasons. Getting this synchronization just right was a long process in human history.

The origins of our modern calendar go back to ancient Egypt. By 4200 B.C., the Egyptians were using a calendar that counted 365 days in a year. However, because the length of a year is about $365\frac{1}{4}$ days (rather than exactly 365 days), the Egyptian calendar drifted out of phase with the seasons by about 1 day every 4 years. For example, if the spring equinox occurred on March 21 one year, 4 years later it occurred on March 22, 4 years after that on March 23, and so on. Over many centuries, the spring equinox moved through many different months. To keep the seasons and the calendar synchronized, Julius Caesar decreed the adoption of a new calendar in 46 B.C. This *Julian calendar* introduced the concept of **leap year**: Every fourth year has 366 days, rather than 365, so that the average length of the calendar year is $365\frac{1}{4}$ days.

The Julian calendar originally had the spring equinox falling around March 24. If it had been perfectly synchronized with the tropical year, this calendar would have ensured that the spring equinox occurred on the same date every 4 years (that is, every leap-year cycle). It didn't work perfectly, however, because a tropical year is actually about 11 minutes short of $365\frac{1}{4}$ days. As a result, the moment of the spring equinox slowly advanced by an average of 11 minutes per year. By the late 16th century, the spring equinox was occurring on March 11.

Concerned by this drift in the date of the spring equinox, Pope Gregory XIII introduced a new calendar in 1582. This *Gregorian calendar* was much like the Julian calendar, with two important adjustments. First, Pope Gregory decreed that the day in 1582 following October 4 would be October 15. By eliminating the 10 dates from October 5 through October 14, 1582, he pushed the date of the spring equinox in 1583 from March 11 to March 21. (He chose March 21 because it was the date of the spring equinox in A.D. 325, which was the time of the Council of Nicaea, the first ecumenical council of the Christian church.) Second, the Gregorian calendar added an exception to the rule of having leap year every 4 years: Leap year is skipped when a century changes (for example, in years 1700, 1800, 1900) *unless* the century year is divisible by 400. Thus, 2000 was a leap year because it is divisible by 400 (2000 ÷ 400 = 5), but 2100 will *not* be a leap year. These adjustments make the average length of the Gregorian calendar year almost exactly the same as the actual length of a tropical year, which ensures that the spring equinox will occur on March 21 every fourth year for thousands of years to come.

Today, the Gregorian calendar is used worldwide for international communication and commerce. (Many countries still use traditional calendars, such as the Chinese, Islamic, and Jewish calendars, for cultural purposes.) However, as you might guess, the pope's decree was not immediately accepted in regions not bound to the Catholic Church. For example, the Gregorian calendar was not adopted in England or in the American colonies until 1752, and it was not adopted in China until 1912 or in Russia until 1919.

S1.2 CELESTIAL COORDINATES AND MOTION IN THE SKY

We are now ready to turn our attention from timekeeping to navigation. The goal of celestial navigation is to use the Sun and the stars to find our position on Earth. Before we can do that, we need to understand the apparent motions of the sky in more detail than we covered in Chapter 2. We'll begin in this section by discussing how we locate objects on the celestial sphere, which will then allow us to explore how positions

Solar Days and the Analemma

The average length of a solar day is 24 hours, but the precise length varies over the course of the year. Two effects contribute to this variation.

The first effect arises from Earth's varying orbital speed. Recall that, in accord with Kepler's second law, Earth moves slightly faster when it is closer to the Sun in its orbit and slightly slower when it is farther from the Sun. Thus, Earth moves slightly farther along its orbit each day when it is closer to the Sun. This means that the solar day requires more than the average amount of "extra" rotation (see Figure S1.2) during these periods—making these solar days longer than average. Similarly, the solar day requires less than the average amount of "extra" rotation when it is in the portion of its orbit farther from the Sun—making these solar days shorter than average.

The second effect arises from the tilt of Earth's axis, which causes the ecliptic to be inclined by $23\frac{1}{2}°$ to the celestial equator on the celestial sphere. Because the length of a solar day depends on the Sun's apparent *eastward* motion along the ecliptic, the inclination would cause solar days to vary in length even if Earth's orbit were perfectly circular. To see why, suppose the Sun appeared to move exactly 1° per day along the ecliptic. Around the times of the solstices, this motion

would be entirely eastward, making the solar day slightly longer than average. Around the times of the equinoxes, when the motion along the ecliptic has a significant northward or southward component, the solar day would be slightly shorter than average.

Together, the two effects make the actual length of solar days up to about 25 seconds longer or shorter than the 24-hour average. Because the effects accumulate at particular times of year, the apparent solar time can differ by as much as 17 minutes from the mean solar time. The net result is often depicted visually by an **analemma** (Figure 1), which looks much like a figure 8. You'll find an analemma printed on many globes, and Figure 2.17 shows a photographic version.

By using the horizontal scale on the analemma, you can convert between mean and apparent solar time for any date. (The vertical scale shows the declination of the Sun, which is discussed in Section S1.2.) For example, the dashed line shows that on November 10, a mean solar clock is about 17 minutes "behind the Sun," or behind apparent solar time. Thus, if the apparent solar time is 6:00 p.m. on November 10, the mean solar time is only 5:43 p.m. The discrepancy between mean and apparent solar times is called the **equation of time**. It is often plotted as a graph (Figure 2), which gives the same results as reading from the analemma.

The discrepancy between mean and apparent solar time also explains why the times of sunrise and sunset don't follow seasonal patterns perfectly. For example, the winter solstice around December 21 has the shortest daylight hours (in the Northern Hemisphere), but the earliest sunset occurs around December 7, when the Sun is still well "behind" mean solar time.

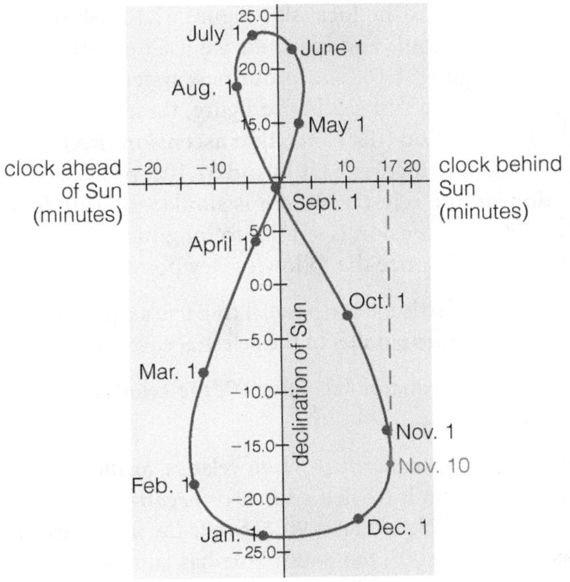

FIGURE 1 The analemma shows the annual pattern of discrepancies between apparent and mean solar time. For example, the dashed red line shows that on November 10, a mean solar clock reads 17 minutes behind (earlier than) apparent solar time.

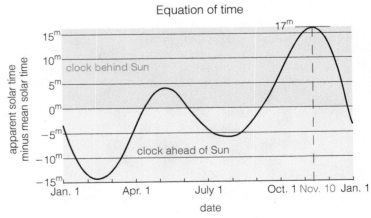

FIGURE 2 The discrepancies can also be plotted on a graph as the equation of time.

on the celestial sphere determine motion in the local sky. With this background, we'll be ready to explore the principles of celestial navigation in the final section of this chapter.

How do we locate objects on the celestial sphere?

Recall from Chapter 2 that the celestial sphere is an illusion, but one that is quite useful when looking at the sky. We can make the celestial sphere even more useful by giving it a set of **celestial coordinates** that function much like the coordinates of latitude and longitude on Earth. Just as we can locate a city on Earth by its latitude and longitude, we can use an object's celestial coordinates to describe its precise location on the celestial sphere.

We have already discussed the basic features of the celestial sphere that will serve as starting points for our coordinate system: the north and south celestial poles, the celestial equator, and the ecliptic. Figure S1.8 shows these locations on a schematic diagram. The arrow along the ecliptic indicates the direction in which the Sun appears to move over the course of each year. It is much easier to visualize the celestial sphere if you make a model with a simple plastic ball. Use a felt-tip pen to mark the north and south celestial poles on your ball, and then add the celestial equator and the ecliptic. Note that the ecliptic crosses the celestial equator on opposite sides of the celestial sphere at an angle of $23\frac{1}{2}°$ (because of the tilt of Earth's axis).

Equinoxes and Solstices Remember that the equinoxes and solstices are special moments in the year that help define the seasons [Section 2.2]. For example, the *spring equinox,* which occurs around March 21 each year, is the moment when spring begins for the Northern Hemisphere and fall begins for the Southern Hemisphere. These moments correspond to positions in Earth's orbit (see Figure 2.15) and hence to apparent locations of the Sun along the ecliptic. As shown in Figure S1.8, the spring equinox occurs when the Sun is on the ecliptic at the point where it crosses from south of the celestial equator to north of the celestial equator. This point is also called the spring equinox. Thus, the term *spring equinox* has a dual meaning: It is the *moment* when spring begins and also the *point* on the ecliptic at which the Sun appears to be located at that moment.

Figure S1.8 also shows the points marking the summer solstice, fall equinox, and winter solstice, with the dates on which the Sun appears to be located at each point. Remember that the dates are approximate because of the leap-year cycle and because a tropical year is not exactly $365\frac{1}{4}$ days. (For example, the spring equinox may occur anytime between about March 20 and March 23.)

Although no bright stars mark the locations of the equinoxes or solstices among the constellations, you can find them with the aid of nearby bright stars (Figure S1.9). For example, the spring equinox is located in the constellation Pisces and can be found with the aid of the four bright stars in the Great Square of Pegasus. Of course, when the Sun is located at this point around March 21, we cannot see Pisces or Pegasus because they are close to the Sun in our daytime sky.

Celestial Coordinates We can now add our system of celestial coordinates to the celestial sphere. Because this will be the third coordinate system we've used in this book, it's easier to understand if we first review the other two. Figure S1.10a shows the coordinates of *altitude* and *direction* (or *azimuth**) we use in the local sky. Figure S1.10b shows the coordinates of *latitude* and *longitude* we use on Earth's surface. Finally, Figure S1.10c shows our new system of celestial coordinates. As you can see in the figure, these coordinates are called **declination (dec)** and **right ascension (RA)**.

If you compare Figures S1.10b and S1.10c, you'll see that declination on the celestial sphere is similar to latitude on Earth and right ascension is similar to longitude. Let's start with declination; notice the following key points:

- Just as lines of latitude are parallel to Earth's equator, lines of declination are parallel to the celestial equator.

- Just as Earth's equator has lat = 0°, the celestial equator has dec = 0°.

- Latitude is labeled *north* or *south* relative to the equator, while declination is labeled *positive* or *negative*. For example, the North Pole has lat = 90°N, while the north celestial pole has dec = +90°; the South Pole has lat = 90°S, while the south celestial pole has dec = −90°.

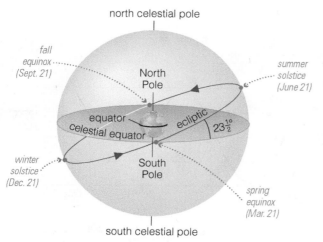

north celestial pole

fall equinox (Sept. 21)

North Pole

summer solstice (June 21)

equator celestial equator

ecliptic

$23\frac{1}{2}°$

winter solstice (Dec. 21)

South Pole

spring equinox (Mar. 21)

south celestial pole

FIGURE S1.8 Schematic diagram of the celestial sphere, shown without stars.

*Azimuth is usually measured clockwise around the horizon from due north. By this definition, the azimuth of due north is 0°, of due east is 90°, of due south is 180°, and of due west is 270°.

These diagrams show the locations among the constellations of the equinoxes and solstices. No bright stars mark any of these points, so you must find them by studying their positions relative to recognizable patterns. The time of day or night at which each point is above the horizon depends on the time of year.

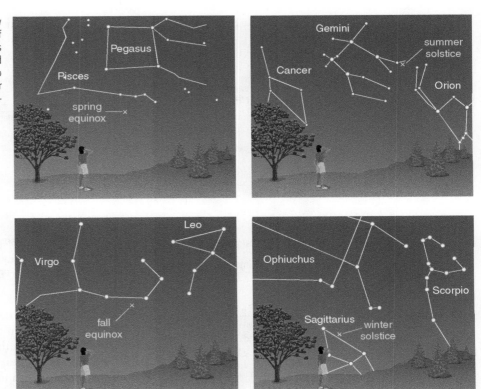

Next, notice the close correspondence between right ascension and longitude:

- Just as lines of longitude extend from the North Pole to the South Pole, lines of right ascension extend from the north celestial pole to the south celestial pole.

- Just as there is no natural starting point for longitude, there is no natural starting point for right ascension. By international treaty, longitude zero (the prime meridian) is the line of longitude that runs through Greenwich, England. By convention, right ascension zero is the line of right ascension that runs through the spring equinox.

- Longitude is measured in *degrees* east or west of Greenwich, while right ascension is measured in *hours* (and minutes and seconds) east of the spring equinox. A full 360° circle around the celestial equator goes through 24 hours of right ascension, so each hour of right ascension represents an angle of $360° \div 24 = 15°$.

As an example of how we use celestial coordinates to locate objects on the celestial sphere, consider the bright star Vega. Its coordinates are dec = +38°44' and RA = 18^h35^m (Figure S1.11). The positive declination tells us that Vega is 38°44' *north* of the celestial equator. The right ascension tells us that Vega is 18 hours 35 minutes east of the spring equinox. Translating the right ascension from hours to angular degrees, we find that Vega is about 279° east of the spring equinox (because 18 hours represents $18 \times 15° = 270°$ and 35 minutes represents $\frac{35}{60} \times 15° \approx 9°$).

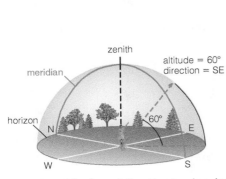

a We use altitude and direction to pinpoint locations in the local sky.

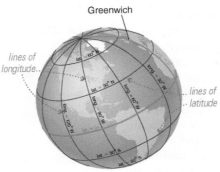

b We use latitude and longitude to pinpoint locations on Earth.

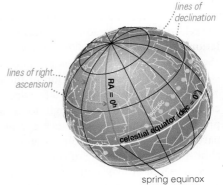

c We use declination and right ascension to pinpoint locations on the celestial sphere.

Celestial coordinate systems.

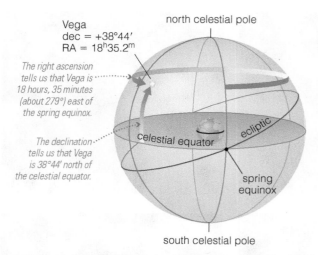

Vega
dec = +38°44'
RA = 18ʰ35.2ᵐ

The right ascension tells us that Vega is 18 hours, 35 minutes (about 279°) east of the spring equinox.

The declination tells us that Vega is 38°44' north of the celestial equator.

north celestial pole

celestial equator

ecliptic

spring equinox

south celestial pole

FIGURE S1.11 This diagram shows how we interpret the celestial coordinates of Vega.

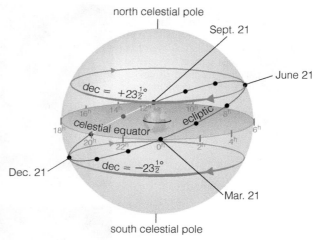

north celestial pole

Sept. 21

June 21

dec = +23½°

celestial equator

ecliptic

Dec. 21

dec = −23½°

Mar. 21

south celestial pole

FIGURE S1.12 We can use this diagram of the celestial sphere to determine the Sun's right ascension and declination at monthly intervals.

The Vega example also shows why right ascension is measured in units of time: It is because time units make it easier to track the daily motions of objects through the local sky. All objects with a particular right ascension cross the meridian at the same time, which means that all stars with RA = 0ʰ cross the meridian at the same time that the spring equinox crosses the meridian. Thus, when we use time units, the right ascension of any object tells us how long *after* the spring equinox the object crosses the meridian. For example, Vega's right ascension, 18ʰ35ᵐ, tells us that on any particular day, Vega crosses the meridian about 18 hours 35 minutes after the spring equinox. (This is 18 hours 35 minutes of *sidereal time* later, which is not exactly the same as 18 hours 35 minutes of solar time; see Mathematical Insight S1.2.)

Stars are so far away that they take thousands of years or more to move noticeably on the celestial sphere. Nevertheless, the celestial coordinates of stars are not quite constant, because they are tied to the celestial equator and the celestial equator gradually moves relative to the constellations with Earth's 26,000-year cycle of axis precession [Section 2.2]. (Axis precession does not affect Earth's orbit, so it does not affect the location of the ecliptic among the constellations.) Even over just a few decades, the coordinate changes are significant enough to make a difference in precise astronomical work—such as aiming a telescope at a particular object. As a result, careful observations require almost constant updating of celestial coordinates. Star catalogs therefore always state the year for which coordinates are given (for example, "epoch 2000"). Astronomical software can automatically calculate day-to-day celestial coordinates for the Sun, Moon, and planets as they wander among the constellations.

Celestial Coordinates of the Sun Unlike stars, which remain fixed in the patterns of the constellations on the celestial sphere, the Sun moves gradually along the ecliptic. It takes a year for the Sun to make a full circuit of the ecliptic, which means it moves through all 24 hours of right ascension over the course of the year. Each month, the Sun moves approximately one-twelfth of the way around the ecliptic, meaning that its right ascension changes by about 24 ÷ 12 = 2 hours per month. Figure S1.12 shows the ecliptic marked with the Sun's monthly position and a scale of celestial coordinates. From this figure, we can create a table of the Sun's month-by-month celestial coordinates.

Table S1.1 starts from the spring equinox, when the Sun has declination 0° and right ascension 0ʰ. You can see in the shaded areas of the table that while RA advances steadily through the year, the Sun's declination changes much more

TABLE S1.1 The Sun's Approximate Celestial Coordinates at 1-Month Intervals

Approximate Date	RA	Dec
Mar. 21 (spring equinox)	0ʰ	0°
Apr. 21	2ʰ	+12°
May 21	4ʰ	+20°
June 21 (summer solstice)	6ʰ	+23½°
July 21	8ʰ	+20°
Aug. 21	10ʰ	+12°
Sept. 21 (fall equinox)	12ʰ	0°
Oct. 21	14ʰ	−12°
Nov. 21	16ʰ	−20°
Dec. 21 (winter solstice)	18ʰ	−23½°
Jan. 21	20ʰ	−20°
Feb. 21	22ʰ	−12°

rapidly around the equinoxes than around the solstices. For example, the Sun's declination changes from $-12°$ on February 21 to $12°$ on April 21, a difference of $24°$ in just 2 months. In contrast, during the 2 months around the summer solstice (that is, between May 21 and July 21), the declination varies only between $+20°$ and its maximum of $+23\frac{1}{2}°$. This behavior explains why the number of daylight hours increases rapidly in spring and decreases rapidly in fall, while the number of daylight hours remains long and nearly constant for a couple of months around the summer solstice and short and nearly constant for a couple of months around the winter solstice.

MATHEMATICAL INSIGHT S1.2

Time by the Stars

The clocks we use in daily life are set to solar time, ticking through 24 hours for each day of mean solar time. In astronomy, it is also useful to have clocks that tell time by the stars, or **sidereal time**. Just as we define *solar time* according to the Sun's position relative to the meridian, *sidereal time* is based on the positions of stars relative to the meridian. We define the **hour angle (HA)** of any object on the celestial sphere to be the time since it last crossed the meridian. (For a circumpolar star, hour angle is measured from the *higher* of the two points at which it crosses the meridian each day.) For example:

■ If a star is crossing the meridian now, its hour angle is 0^h.

■ If a star crossed the meridian 3 hours ago, its hour angle is 3^h.

■ If a star will cross the meridian 1 hour from now, its hour angle is -1^h or, equivalently, 23^h.

By convention, time by the stars is based on the hour angle of the spring equinox. That is, the **local sidereal time (LST)** is

$$LST = HA_{\text{spring equinox}}$$

For example, the local sidereal time is 00:00 when the spring equinox is *on* the meridian. Three hours later, when the spring equinox is 3 hours west of the meridian, the local sidereal time is 03:00.

Note that, because right ascension tells us how long after the spring equinox an object reaches the meridian, the local sidereal time is also equal to the right ascension (RA) of objects currently crossing your meridian. For example, if your local sidereal time is 04:30, stars with $RA = 4^h30^m$ are currently crossing your meridian. This idea leads to an important relationship among any object's current hour angle, the current local sidereal time, and the object's right ascension:

$$HA_{\text{object}} = LST - RA_{\text{object}}$$

This formula will make sense to you if you recognize that an object's right ascension tells us the time by which it trails the spring equinox on its daily trek through the sky. Because the local sidereal time tells us how long it has been since the spring equinox was on the meridian, the difference $LST - RA_{\text{object}}$ must tell us the position of the object relative to the meridian.

Sidereal time has one important subtlety: Because the stars (and the celestial sphere) appear to rotate around us in one sidereal day (23^h56^m), sidereal clocks must tick through 24 hours of sidereal time in 23 hours 56 minutes of solar time. That is, a sidereal clock gains about 4 minutes per day over a solar clock. As a result, you cannot immediately infer the local sidereal time from the local solar time, or vice versa, without either doing some calculations or consulting an astronomical table. Of course, the easiest way to determine the local sidereal time is with a clock that ticks at the sidereal rate. Astronomical observatories always have sidereal clocks, and you can buy moderately priced telescopes that come with sidereal clocks.

EXAMPLE 1: Suppose the local apparent solar time is 9:00 p.m. on the spring equinox (March 21). What is the local sidereal time?

SOLUTION:

Step 1 Understand: The trick to this problem is understanding exactly what we are looking for. We are asked to find the local sidereal time, which is defined as the hour angle of the spring equinox in the local sky. Thus, we need to know where the spring equinox is located in the local sky. We are given the key clue: The date is the day of the spring equinox, the one day of the year on which the Sun is located in the same position as the spring equinox in the sky.

Step 2 Solve: We can now find the hour angle of the spring equinox from the hour angle of the Sun. We are told that the local apparent solar time is 9:00 p.m., which means that the Sun is 9 hours past the meridian and thus has an hour angle of 9 hours. Because the spring equinox and the Sun are located in the same place on this one date of the year, the hour angle of the spring equinox is also 9 hours.

Step 3 Explain: The hour angle of the spring equinox is 9 hours, which means the local sidereal time is $LST = 09:00$.

EXAMPLE 2: Suppose the local sidereal time is $LST = 04:00$. When will Vega cross the meridian?

SOLUTION:

Step 1 Understand: We are given the local sidereal time, which tells us the hour angle of the spring equinox in the local sky. To determine when Vega will cross the meridian, we need to know its hour angle, which we can calculate from its right ascension and the formula given above. Figure S1.11 shows us that Vega has $RA = 18^h35^m$, so we have all the information we need.

Step 2 Solve: We now use the formula to find Vega's hour angle from the local sidereal time and Vega's right ascension:

$$HA_{\text{Vega}} = LST - RA_{\text{Vega}} = 4:00 - 18:35 = -14:35$$

Step 3 Explain: Vega's hour angle is -14 hours 35 minutes, which means it will cross your meridian 14 hours and 35 minutes from now. This also means that Vega crossed your meridian 9 hours and 25 minutes ago (because $14^h35^m + 9^h25^m = 24^h$). Note that these are intervals of sidereal time.

How do stars move through the local sky?

We can use our system of celestial coordinates to gain a better understanding of the way stars move through the local sky. Earth's rotation makes all celestial objects appear to circle around Earth each day (see Figure 2.9), but what we actually see in the local sky is more complex because we see only half the celestial sphere at one time (the ground blocks our view of the other half). Let's explore the appearance of the local sky. As we'll see, the path of any star through your local sky depends on only two things: (1) your latitude and (2) the declination of the star whose path you want to know.

The Sky at the North Pole The daily paths of stars are easiest to understand for the local sky at the North Pole, so let's begin there before moving on to other latitudes. Figure S1.13a shows the rotating celestial sphere and your orientation relative to it when you are standing at the North Pole. Your "up" points toward the north celestial pole, which therefore marks your zenith. Earth blocks your view of anything south of the celestial equator, which therefore runs along your horizon. To make it easier for you to visualize the local sky, Figure S1.13b shows your horizon extending to the celestial sphere. The horizon is marked with directions, but remember that all directions are south from the North Pole. We therefore cannot define a meridian for the North Pole, since a meridian would have to run from the north to the south points on the horizon and there are no such unique points at the North Pole.

Notice that the daily circles of the stars keep them at constant altitudes above or below the North Polar horizon. Moreover, the altitude of any star is equal to its declination. For example, a star with declination +60° circles the sky at an altitude of 60°, and a star with declination −30° remains 30° below your horizon at all times. As a result, all stars north of the celestial equator are circumpolar at the North Pole, meaning that they never fall below the horizon. Stars south of the celestial equator can never be seen at the North Pole. If you are having difficulty visualizing the star paths, it may help you to watch star paths as you rotate your plastic ball model of the celestial sphere.

You should also notice that right ascension does not affect a star's path at all: The path depends only on declination. As we'll see shortly, this rule holds for all latitudes. Right ascension affects only the *time* of day and year at which a star is found in a particular position in your sky.

The Sky at the Equator After the Poles, the equatorial sky is the next easiest case to understand. Imagine that you are standing somewhere on Earth's equator (lat = 0°), such as in Ecuador, in Kenya, or on the island of Borneo. Figure S1.14a shows that "up" points directly away from (perpendicular to) Earth's rotation axis. Figure S1.14b shows the local sky more clearly by extending the horizon to the celestial sphere and rotating the diagram so the zenith is up. As it does everywhere except at the poles, the meridian extends from the horizon due south, through the zenith, to the horizon due north.

Look carefully at how the celestial sphere appears to rotate in the local sky. The north celestial pole remains stationary on your horizon due north. As we should expect, its altitude of 0° is equal to the equator's latitude [Section 2.1]. Similarly, the south celestial pole remains stationary on your horizon due south. At any particular time, half the celestial equator is visible, extending from the horizon due east, through the zenith, to the horizon due west. The other half lies below the horizon. As the equatorial sky appears to turn, all star paths rise straight out of the eastern horizon and set straight into the western horizon, with the following features:

- **Stars with dec = 0°** lie *on* the celestial equator and therefore rise due east, cross the meridian at the zenith, and set due west.

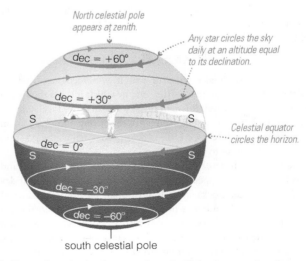

north celestial pole

dec = +60°

dec = +30°

celestial equator

dec = 0°

dec = −30°

dec = −60°

south celestial pole

a The orientation of the local sky, relative to the celestial sphere, for an observer at the North Pole.

North celestial pole appears at zenith.

Any star circles the sky daily at an altitude equal to its declination.

dec = +60°

dec = +30°

S   S

dec = 0°

S   S

Celestial equator circles the horizon.

dec = −30°

dec = −60°

south celestial pole

b Extending the horizon to the celestial sphere makes it easier to visualize the local sky at the North Pole.

FIGURE S1.13 The sky at the North Pole.

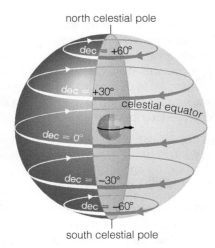

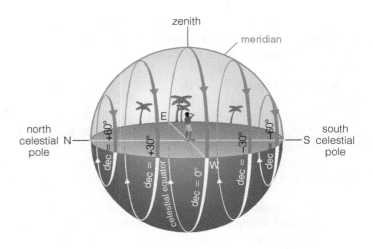

a The orientation of the local sky, relative to the celestial sphere, for an observer at Earth's equator.

b Extending the horizon and rotating the diagram make it easier to visualize the local sky at the equator.

FIGURE S1.14 **FIGURE S1.14** The sky at the equator.

- **Stars with dec > 0°** rise north of due east, reach their highest point on the meridian in the north, and set north of due west. Their rise, set, and highest point depend on their declination. For example, a star with dec = +30° rises 30° north of due east, crosses the meridian 30° to the north of the zenith—that is, at an *altitude* of 90° − 30° = 60° in the north—and sets 30° north of due west.

- **Stars with dec < 0°** rise south of due east, reach their highest point on the meridian in the south, and set south of due west. For example, a star with dec = −50° rises 50° south of due east, crosses the meridian 50° to the south of the zenith—that is, at an *altitude* of 90° − 50° = 40° in the south—and sets 50° south of due west.

Notice that exactly half of any star's daily circle lies above the horizon, which means that every star at the equator is above the horizon for exactly half of each sidereal day, or just

under 12 hours, and below the horizon for the other half of the sidereal day. Also, notice again that right ascension does not affect star paths, although it does affect the time of day and year at which a star will be in a particular place along its path.

THINK ABOUT IT

Are any stars circumpolar at the equator? Are there stars that never rise above the horizon at the equator? Explain.

Skies at Other Latitudes Star tracks may at first seem more complex at other latitudes, with their mixtures of circumpolar stars and stars that rise and set. However, they are easy to understand if we apply the same basic strategy we've used for the North Pole and equator. Let's consider latitude 40°N, such as in Denver, Indianapolis, Philadelphia, or Beijing. First, as shown in Figure S1.15a, imagine standing at this latitude on a basic diagram of the rotating celestial sphere. Note

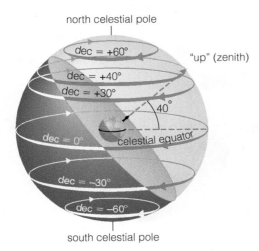

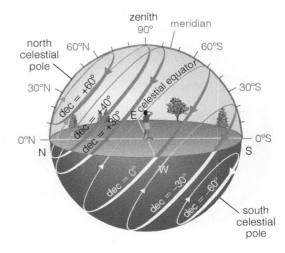

a The orientation of the local sky, relative to the celestial sphere, for an observer at latitude 40°N. Because latitude is the angle to Earth's equator, "up" points to the circle on the celestial sphere with declination +40°.

b Extending the horizon and rotating the diagram so the zenith is up make it easier to visualize the local sky. The blue scale along the meridian shows altitudes and directions in the local sky.

FIGURE S1.15 The sky at 40°N latitude.

that "up" points to a location on the celestial sphere with declination +40°. To make it easier to visualize the local sky, we next extend the horizon and rotate the diagram so the zenith is up (Figure S1.15b).

As we would expect, the north celestial pole appears 40° above the horizon due north, since its altitude in the local sky is always equal to your latitude. Half the celestial equator is visible. It extends from the horizon due east, to the meridian at an altitude of 50° in the south, to the horizon due west. By comparing this diagram to that of the local sky for the equator, you'll notice the following general rule that applies to all latitudes except the poles:

> **The celestial equator always extends from due east on your horizon to due west on your horizon, crossing the meridian at an altitude of 90° *minus* your latitude.**

The celestial equator crosses the meridian south of the zenith for locations in the Northern Hemisphere and north of the zenith for locations in the Southern Hemisphere.

If you study Figure S1.15b carefully, you'll notice the following features of the sky for latitude 40°N:

- **Stars with dec = 0°** lie *on* the celestial equator and therefore follow the path of the celestial equator through the local sky. That is, for latitude 40°N, these stars rise due east, cross the meridian at altitude 90° − 40° = 50° in the south, and set due west.

- **Stars with dec > (90° − lat)** are circumpolar. Thus, for latitude 40°N, stars with declination greater than 90° − 40° = 50° are circumpolar, because they lie *within* 40° of the north celestial pole.

- **Stars with dec > 0° but that are not circumpolar** follow paths parallel to but north of the celestial equator: They rise north of due east and set north of due west, and cross the meridian to the north of the place where the celestial equator crosses it by an amount equal to their declination. For example, because the celestial equator at latitude 40° crosses the meridian at altitude 50° in the south, a star with dec = +30° crosses the meridian at altitude 50° + 30° = 80° in the south. Similarly, a star with dec = +60° crosses the meridian 60° farther north than the celestial equator, which means at altitude 70° in the north. (To calculate this result, note that the sum 50° + 60° = 110° goes 20° past the zenith altitude of 90°, making it equivalent to 90° − 20° = 70°.)

- **Stars with dec < (−90° + lat)** never rise above the horizon. Thus, for latitude 40°N, stars with declination less than −90° + 40° = −50° never rise above the horizon, because they lie within 40° of the south celestial pole.

- **Stars with dec < 0° but that are sometimes visible** follow paths parallel to but south of the celestial equator: They rise south of due east and set south of due west, and cross the meridian south of the place where the celestial equator crosses it by an amount equal to their declination. For example, a star with dec = −30° crosses the meridian at altitude 50° − 30° = 20° in the south.

You should also notice that the fraction of any star's daily circle that is above the horizon—and hence the amount of time it is above the horizon each day—depends on its declination. Because exactly half the celestial equator is above the horizon, stars on the celestial equator (dec = 0°) are above the horizon for about 12 hours per day. For northern latitudes like 40°N, stars with positive declinations have more than half their daily circles above the horizon and hence are above the horizon for more than 12 hours each day (with the range extending to 24 hours a day for the circumpolar stars). Stars with negative declinations have less than half their daily circles above the horizon and hence are above the horizon for less than 12 hours each day (with the range going to zero for stars that are never above the horizon).

We can apply the same strategy we used in Figure S1.15 to find star paths for other latitudes. Figure S1.16 shows the local

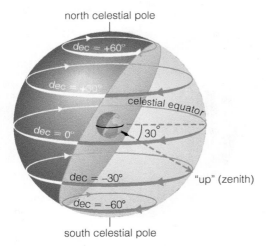

a The orientation of the local sky for an observer at latitude 30°S, relative to the celestial sphere. "Up" points to the circle on the celestial sphere with dec = −30°.

FIGURE S1.16 The sky at 30°S latitude.

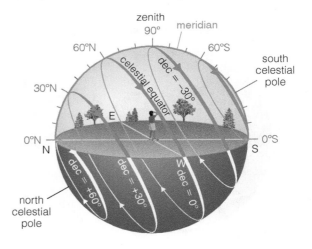

b Extending the horizon and rotating the diagram so the zenith is up make it easier to visualize the local sky. Note that the south celestial pole is visible at altitude 30° in the south, while the celestial equator stretches across the northern half of the sky.

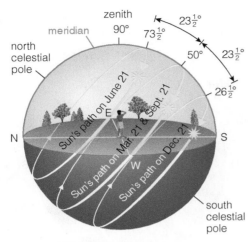

FIGURE S1.17 [Interactive Figure] The Sun's daily path on the equinoxes and solstices at latitude 40°N.

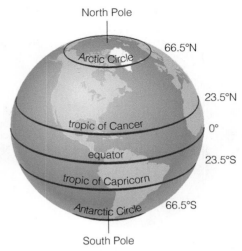

FIGURE S1.18 Special latitudes defined by the Sun's path through the sky.

sky for latitude 30°S. Note that the south celestial pole is visible to the south and that the celestial equator passes through the northern half of the sky. If you study the diagram carefully, you can see how star tracks depend on declination.

THINK ABOUT IT

Study Figure S1.16 for latitude 30°S. Describe the path of the celestial equator. Does it obey the 90° − latitude rule given earlier? Describe how star tracks differ for stars with positive and negative declinations. What declination must a star have to be circumpolar at this latitude?

How does the Sun move through the local sky?

Like the stars and other objects on the celestial sphere, the Sun's path depends only on its declination and your latitude. However, because the Sun's declination changes over the course of the year, the Sun's path also changes.

Figure S1.17 shows the Sun's path on the equinoxes and solstices for latitude 40°N. On the equinoxes, the Sun is on the celestial equator (dec = 0°) and therefore follows the celestial equator's path: It rises due east, crosses the meridian at altitude 50° in the south, and sets due west. Like any object on the celestial equator, it is above the horizon for 12 hours. On the summer solstice, when the Sun has dec = $+23\frac{1}{2}°$ (see Table S1.1), the Sun rises well north of due east,* reaches an altitude of $50° + 23\frac{1}{2}° = 73\frac{1}{2}°$ when it crosses the meridian in the south, and sets well north of due west. The daylight hours are long because much more than half the Sun's path is above the horizon. On the winter solstice, when the Sun has dec = $-23\frac{1}{2}°$, the Sun rises well south of due east, reaches an altitude of only $50° - 23\frac{1}{2}° = 26\frac{1}{2}°$ when it crosses the meridian in the south,

and sets well south of due west. The daylight hours are short because much less than half the Sun's path is above the horizon.

We could make a similar diagram to show the Sun's path on various dates for any latitude. However, the $23\frac{1}{2}°$ tilt of Earth's axis makes the Sun's path particularly interesting at the special latitudes shown in Figure S1.18. Let's investigate.

The Sun at the North and South Poles Remember that the celestial equator circles the horizon at the North Pole. Figure S1.19 shows how we use this fact to find the Sun's path in the North Polar sky. Because the Sun appears *on* the celestial equator on the day of the spring equinox, the Sun circles the North Polar sky *on the horizon* on March 21, completing a full circle in 24 hours (1 solar day). Over the next 3 months, the Sun continues to circle the horizon each day, circling at gradually higher altitudes as its declination increases. It reaches its highest point on the summer solstice, when its declination of $+23\frac{1}{2}°$ means that it circles the North Polar sky at an altitude of $23\frac{1}{2}°$. After the summer solstice, the daily circles gradually fall lower over the next 3 months, reaching

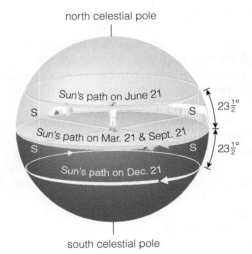

FIGURE S1.19 [Interactive Figure] Daily path of the Sun on the equinoxes and solstices at the North Pole.

---

*Calculating exactly how far north of due east the Sun rises is beyond the scope of this book, but *SkyGazer, Starry Night,* and other astronomical software packages can tell you exactly where (and at what time) the Sun rises and sets each day.

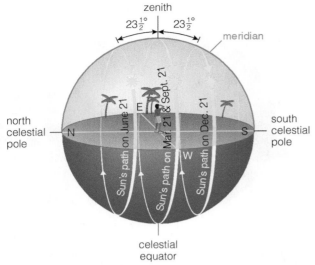

FIGURE S1.20 Interactive Figure ➤ Daily path of the Sun on the equinoxes and solstices at the equator.

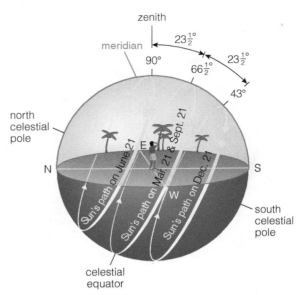

FIGURE S1.21 Interactive Figure ➤ Daily path of the Sun on the equinoxes and solstices at the tropic of Cancer.

the horizon on the fall equinox. Then, because the Sun's declination is negative for the next 6 months (until the following spring equinox), it remains below the North Polar horizon. Thus, the North Pole essentially has 6 months of daylight and 6 months of darkness, with an extended twilight that lasts a few weeks beyond the fall equinox and an extended dawn that begins a few weeks before the spring equinox.

The situation is the opposite at the South Pole. Here the Sun's daily circle first reaches the horizon on the fall equinox. The daily circles then rise gradually higher, reaching a maximum altitude of $23\frac{1}{2}°$ on the *winter* solstice, and then slowly fall back to the horizon on the spring equinox. Thus, the South Pole has the Sun above the horizon during the 6 months it is below the North Polar horizon.

Although we've correctly described the Sun's true position in the polar skies over the course of the year, two effects complicate what we actually see at the poles around the times of the equinoxes. First, the atmosphere bends light enough so that the Sun *appears* to be slightly above the horizon even when it is actually slightly below it. Near the horizon, this bending makes the Sun appear about 1° higher than it would in the absence of an atmosphere. Second, the Sun's angular size of about $\frac{1}{2}°$ means that it does not fall below the horizon at a single moment but instead sets gradually. Together, these effects mean that the Sun appears above each polar horizon for slightly longer (by several days) than 6 months each year.

The Sun at the Equator At the equator, the celestial equator extends from the horizon due east, through the zenith, to the horizon due west. The Sun therefore follows this path on each equinox, reaching the zenith at local noon (Figure S1.20). Following the spring equinox, the Sun's increasing declination means that it follows a daily track that takes it gradually northward in the sky. It is farthest north on the summer solstice, when it rises $23\frac{1}{2}°$ north of due east, crosses the meridian at altitude $90° - 23\frac{1}{2}° = 66\frac{1}{2}°$ in the north, and sets $23\frac{1}{2}°$ north of due west. Over the next 6 months, it gradually tracks southward until the winter

solstice, when its path is the mirror image (across the celestial equator) of its summer solstice path.

Like all objects in the equatorial sky, the Sun is always above the horizon for half a day and below it for half a day. Moreover, the Sun's track is highest in the sky on the equinoxes and lowest on the summer and winter solstices. That is why equatorial regions do not have four seasons like temperate regions [Section 2.2]. The Sun's path in the equatorial sky also makes it rise and set perpendicular to the horizon every day of the year, making for a more rapid dawn and a briefer twilight than at other latitudes.

The Sun at the Tropics The circles of latitude 23.5°N and 23.5°S are called the **tropic of Cancer** and the **tropic of Capricorn**, respectively (see Figure S1.18). The region between these two circles, generally called the *tropics*, represents the parts of Earth where the Sun can sometimes reach the zenith at noon.

Figure S1.21 shows why the tropic of Cancer is special. The celestial equator extends from due east on the horizon to due west on the horizon, crossing the meridian in the south at an altitude of $90° - 23\frac{1}{2}°$ (the latitude) $= 66\frac{1}{2}°$. The Sun follows this path on the equinoxes (March 21 and September 21). As a result, the Sun's path on the summer solstice, when it crosses the meridian $23\frac{1}{2}°$ northward of the celestial equator, takes it to the zenith at local noon. Because the Sun has its maximum declination on the summer solstice, the tropic of Cancer marks the northernmost latitude at which the Sun ever reaches the zenith. Similarly, at the tropic of Capricorn, the Sun reaches the zenith at local noon on the winter solstice, making this the southernmost latitude at which the Sun ever reaches the zenith. Between the two tropic circles, the Sun passes through the zenith twice a year; the precise dates vary with latitude.

The Sun at the Arctic and Antarctic Circles At the equator, the Sun is above the horizon for 12 hours each day year-round. At latitudes progressively farther from the equator, the daily time that the Sun is above the horizon varies

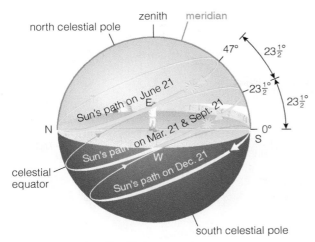

north celestial pole

zenith   meridian

47° $23\frac{1}{2}°$

$23\frac{1}{2}°$ $23\frac{1}{2}°$

N

E

Sun's path on June 21

Sun's path on Mar. 21 & Sept. 21

0°

S

W

Sun's path on Dec. 21

celestial
equator

south celestial pole

FIGURE S1.22 Interactive Figure. Daily path of the Sun on the equinoxes and solstices at the Arctic Circle.

progressively more with the seasons. The special latitudes at which the Sun remains continuously above the horizon for a full day each year are the polar circles: the **Arctic Circle** at latitude 66.5°N and the **Antarctic Circle** at latitude 66.5°S (see Figure S1.18). Poleward of these circles, the length of continuous daylight (or darkness) increases beyond 24 hours, reaching the extreme of 6 months at the North and South Poles.

Figure S1.22 shows why the Arctic Circle is special. The celestial equator extends from due east on the horizon to due west on the horizon, crossing the meridian in the south at an altitude of $90° - 66\frac{1}{2}°$ (the latitude) $= 23\frac{1}{2}°$. As a result, the Sun's path is circumpolar on the summer solstice: It skims the northern horizon at midnight, rises through the eastern sky to a noon maximum altitude of 47° in the south (which is the celestial equator's maximum altitude of $23\frac{1}{2}°$ plus the Sun's summer solstice declination of $23\frac{1}{2}°$), and then gradually falls through the western sky until it is back on the horizon at midnight (see the photograph of this path in Figure 2.18). At the Antarctic Circle, the Sun follows the same basic pattern on the winter solstice, except that it skims the horizon in the south and rises to a noon maximum altitude of 47° in the north.

However, as at the North and South Poles, what we actually see at the polar circles is slightly different from this idealization. Again, the bending of light by Earth's atmosphere and the Sun's angular size of about $\frac{1}{2}°$ make the Sun *appear* to be slightly above the horizon even when it is slightly below it. Thus, the Sun seems not to set for several days, rather than for a single day, around the summer solstice at the Arctic Circle (the winter solstice at the Antarctic Circle). Similarly, the Sun appears to peek above the horizon momentarily, rather than not at all, around the winter solstice at the Arctic Circle (the summer solstice at the Antarctic Circle).

S1.3 PRINCIPLES OF CELESTIAL NAVIGATION

We now have all the background we need to cover the basic principles of celestial navigation. Imagine that you're on a ship at sea, far from any landmarks. How can you figure out where you are? It's easy if you understand the apparent motions of the sky that we have already discussed in this chapter.

How can you determine your latitude?

Determining latitude is particularly easy if you can find the north or south celestial pole: Your latitude is equal to the altitude of the celestial pole in your sky. In the Northern Hemisphere at night, you can determine your approximate latitude by measuring the altitude of Polaris. Because Polaris has a declination within 1° of the north celestial pole, its altitude is within 1° of your latitude. For example, if Polaris has altitude 17°, your latitude is between 16°N and 18°N.

If you want to be more precise, you can determine your latitude from the altitude of *any* star as it crosses your meridian. For example, suppose Vega happens to be crossing your meridian right now and it appears in your southern sky at altitude 78°44'. Because Vega has dec = +38°44' (see Figure S1.11), it crosses your meridian 38°44' north of the celestial equator. As shown in Figure S1.23a, you can conclude that the celestial equator crosses your meridian at an altitude of precisely 40° in the south. Your latitude must therefore be 50°N because the celestial equator always crosses the meridian at an altitude of 90° minus the latitude. You know you are in the Northern Hemisphere because the celestial equator crosses the meridian in the south.

In the daytime, you can find your latitude from the Sun's altitude on your meridian if you know the date and have a table that tells you the Sun's declination on that date. For example, suppose the date is March 21 and the Sun crosses your meridian at altitude 70° in the north (Figure S1.23b). Because the Sun has dec = 0° on March 21, you can conclude that the celestial equator also crosses your meridian in the north at altitude 70°. You must be in the Southern Hemisphere, because the celestial equator crosses the meridian in the north. From the rule that the celestial equator crosses the meridian at an altitude of 90° minus the latitude, you can conclude that you are at latitude 20°S.

How can you determine your longitude?

You can determine your longitude by comparing the current position of an object in your sky with its position as seen from some known longitude. As a simple example, suppose you use a sundial to determine that the apparent solar time is 1:00 p.m., which means the Sun passed the meridian 1 hour ago. You immediately call a friend in England and learn that it is 3:00 p.m. in Greenwich (or you carry a clock that keeps Greenwich time). You now know that your local time is 2 hours earlier than the local time in Greenwich, which means you are 2 hours west of Greenwich. (An earlier time means that you are *west* of Greenwich, because Earth rotates from west to east.) Each hour corresponds to 15° of longitude, so "2 hours west of Greenwich" means longitude 30°W.

At night, you can find your longitude by comparing the positions of stars in your local sky and at some known longitude. For example, suppose Vega is on your meridian and a call to your friend reveals that it won't cross the meridian in Greenwich until 6 hours from now. In this case, your local time is 6 hours later than the local time

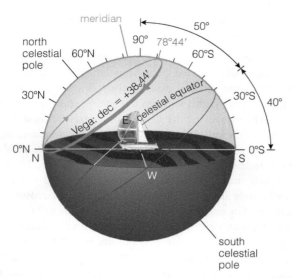

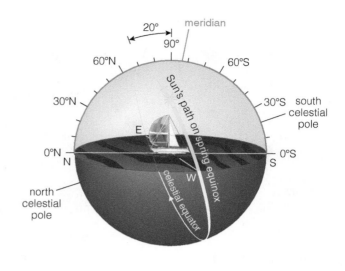

a Because Vega has dec = +38°44′, it crosses the meridian 38°44′ north of the celestial equator. Because Vega crosses the meridian at altitude 78°44′ in the south, the celestial equator must cross the meridian at altitude 40° in the south. Thus, the latitude must be 50°N.

b To determine latitude from the Sun's meridian crossing, you must know the Sun's declination, which you can determine from the date. The case shown is for the spring equinox, when the Sun's declination is 0° and hence follows the path of the celestial equator through the local sky. Because the celestial equator crosses the meridian at 70° in the north, the latitude must be 20°S.

FIGURE S1.23 Determining latitude from a star and from the Sun.

in Greenwich. Thus, you are 6 hours east of Greenwich, or at longitude 90°E (because 6 × 15° = 90°).

Celestial Navigation in Practice Although celestial navigation is easy in principle, at least three considerations make it more difficult in practice. First, finding either latitude or longitude requires a tool for measuring angles in the sky. One such device, called an *astrolabe,* was invented by the ancient Greeks and significantly improved by Islamic scholars during the Middle Ages. The astrolabe's faceplate (Figure S1.24a) could be used to tell time, because it consisted of a rotating star map and horizon plates for specific latitudes. Today you can buy similar rotatable star maps, called *planispheres.* Most astrolabes contained a sighting stick on the back that allowed users to measure the altitudes of bright stars in the sky. These measurements could then be correlated against special markings under the faceplate (Figure S1.24b). Astrolabes were effective but difficult and expensive to make. As a result, medieval sailors often measured angles with a simple pair of calibrated perpendicular sticks, called a *cross-staff* or *Jacob's staff* (Figure S1.24c). A more modern device called a *sextant* allows much more precise angle determinations by incorporating a small telescope for sightings (Figure S1.24d). Sextants are still used for celestial navigation on many ships. If you want to practice celestial navigation yourself, you can buy an inexpensive plastic sextant at many science-oriented stores.

A second practical consideration is knowing the celestial coordinates of stars and the Sun so that you can determine their paths through the local sky. At night, you can use a table listing the celestial coordinates of bright stars. In addition to knowing the celestial coordinates, you must either know the constellations and bright stars extremely well or

carry star charts to help you identify them. For navigating by the Sun in the daytime, you'll need a table listing the Sun's celestial coordinates on each day of the year.

The third practical consideration applies to determining longitude: You need to know the current position of the Sun (or a particular star) in a known location, such as Greenwich, England. Although you could determine this by calling a friend who lives there, it's more practical to carry a clock set to universal time (that is, Greenwich mean time). In the daytime, the clock makes it easy to determine your longitude. If apparent solar time is 1:00 p.m. in your location and the clock tells you that it is 3:00 p.m. in Greenwich, then you are 2 hours west of Greenwich, or at longitude 30°W. The task is more difficult at night, because you must compare the position of a *star* in your sky to its current position in Greenwich. You can do this with the aid of detailed astronomical tables that allow you to determine the current position of any star in the Greenwich sky from the date and the universal time.

Historically, this third consideration created enormous problems for navigation. Before the invention of accurate clocks, sailors could easily determine their latitude but not their longitude. Indeed, most of the European voyages of discovery in the 15th century through the 17th century relied on little more than guesswork about longitude, although some sailors learned complex mathematical techniques for estimating longitude through observations of the lunar phases. More accurate longitude determination, upon which the development of extensive ocean commerce and travel depended, required the invention of a clock that would remain accurate on a ship rocking in the ocean swells. By the early 18th century, solving this problem was considered so important that the British government offered a substantial monetary prize for the solution. John Harrison claimed the prize in

a The faceplate of an astrolabe; many astrolabes had sighting sticks on the back for measuring positions of bright stars.

b A copper engraving of Italian explorer Amerigo Vespucci (for whom America was named) using an astrolabe to sight the Southern Cross. The engraving by Philip Galle, from the book *Nova Reperta*, was based on an original by Joannes Stradanus in the early 1580s.

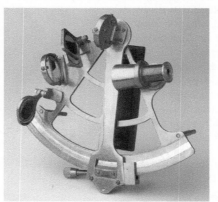

d A sextant.

c A woodcutting of Ptolemy holding a cross-staff (artist unknown).

FIGURE S1.24 Navigational instruments.

1761, with a clock that lost only 5 seconds during a 9-week voyage to Jamaica.*

The Global Positioning System In the past couple of decades, a new type of celestial navigation has supplanted traditional methods. It finds positions relative to a set of satellites in Earth orbit. These satellites of the **global positioning system (GPS)** in essence function like artificial stars. The satellites' positions at any moment are known precisely from their orbital characteristics. The GPS currently uses about two dozen satellites orbiting Earth at an altitude of 20,000 kilometers. Each satellite transmits a radio signal that a small radio receiver can pick up—rain or shine, day or night. Each GPS receiver has a built-in computer that calculates your precise position on Earth by comparing the signals received from several GPS satellites.

The United States originally built the GPS in the late 1970s for military use. Today, the many applications of the GPS include automobile navigation systems as well as systems for helping airplanes land safely, guiding the blind around town, and helping lost hikers find their way. Geologists have used the GPS to measure *millimeter*-scale changes in Earth's crust.

With rapid growth in the use of GPS navigation, the ancient practice of celestial navigation is in danger of becoming a lost art. Fortunately, many amateur clubs and societies are keeping the skills of celestial navigation alive.

COMMON MISCONCEPTIONS

Compass Directions

Most people determine direction with the aid of a compass rather than the stars. However, a compass needle doesn't actually point to true geographic north. Instead, the compass needle responds to Earth's magnetic field and points to *magnetic* north, which can be substantially different from true north. If you want to navigate precisely with a compass, you need a special map that takes into account local variations in Earth's magnetic field. Such maps are available at most camping stores. They are not perfectly reliable, however, because the magnetic field also varies with time. In general, celestial navigation is much more reliable for determining direction than using a compass.

*The story of the difficulties surrounding the measurement of longitude at sea and how Harrison finally solved the problem is chronicled in *Longitude*, by Dava Sobel (Walker and Company, 1995).

Putting Chapter S1 into Context

In this chapter, we built upon concepts from the first three chapters to form a more detailed understanding of celestial timekeeping and navigation. We also learned how to determine paths for the Sun and the stars in the local sky. As you look back at what you've learned, keep in mind the following "big picture" ideas:

- Our modern systems of timekeeping are rooted in the apparent motions of the Sun through the sky. Although it's easy to forget these roots when you look at a clock or a calendar, the sky was the only guide to time for most of human history.

- The term *celestial navigation* sounds a bit mysterious, but it refers to simple principles that allow you to determine your location on Earth. Even if you're never lost at sea, you may find the basic techniques of celestial navigation useful to orient yourself at night (for example, on your next camping trip).

- If you understand the apparent motions of the sky discussed in this chapter and also learn the constellations and bright stars, you'll feel very much "at home" under the stars at night.

SUMMARY OF KEY CONCEPTS

S1.1 ASTRONOMICAL TIME PERIODS

- **How do we define the day, month, year, and planetary periods?** Each of these is defined in two ways. A **sidereal day** is Earth's rotation period, which is about 4 minutes shorter than the 24-hour **solar day** from noon one day to noon the next day. A **sidereal month** is the Moon's orbital period of about $27\frac{1}{3}$ days; a **synodic month** is the $29\frac{1}{2}$ days required for the Moon's cycle of phases. A **sidereal year** is Earth's orbital period, which is about 20 minutes longer than the **tropical year** from one spring equinox to the next. A

  planet's **sidereal period** is its orbital period, and its **synodic period** is the time from one opposition or conjunction to the next.

- **How do we tell the time of day?** There are several time measurement systems. **Apparent solar time** is based on the Sun's position in the local sky. **Mean solar time** is also local, but it averages the changes in the Sun's rate of motion over the year. **Standard time** and **daylight saving time** divide the world into time zones. **Universal time** is the mean solar time in Greenwich, England.

- **When and why do we have leap years?** We usually have a **leap year** every 4 years because the length of the year is about $365\frac{1}{4}$ days. However, it is not exactly $365\frac{1}{4}$ days, so our calendar skips a leap year in century years not divisible by 400.

S1.2 CELESTIAL COORDINATES AND MOTION IN THE SKY

- **How do we locate objects on the celestial sphere?** **Declination** is given as an angle describing an object's position north or south of the celestial equator. **Right ascension**, usually measured in hours (and minutes and seconds), tells us how far east an object is located relative to the spring equinox.

- **How do stars move through the local sky?** A star's path through the local sky depends on its declination and your latitude. Latitude tells you the orientation of your sky relative to the celestial sphere, while declination tells you how a particular star's path compares to the path of the celestial equator through your sky.

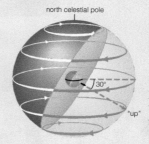

- **How does the Sun move through the local sky?** The Sun's path also depends on its declination and your latitude, but it varies throughout the year because of the Sun's changing declination. The Sun's varying path helps define special latitudes, including the **tropics of Cancer** and **Capricorn** and the **Arctic** and **Antarctic Circles**.

S1.3 PRINCIPLES OF CELESTIAL NAVIGATION

- **How can you determine your latitude?** You can determine your latitude from the altitude of the celestial pole in your sky or by measuring the altitude and knowing the declination of a star (or the Sun) as it crosses your meridian.

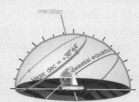

- **How can you determine your longitude?** To determine longitude you must know the position of the Sun or a star in your sky and its position at the same time in the sky of Greenwich, England (or some other specific location). This is most easily done if you have a clock that tells universal time.

REVIEW QUESTIONS

Short-Answer Questions Based on the Reading

1. Why is a *sidereal day* shorter than a *solar day*?

2. What is the difference between a *sidereal month* and a *synodic month*? Between a *sidereal year* and a *tropical year*? Between a planet's *sidereal period* and its *synodic period*?

3. What do we mean by *opposition, conjunction,* and *greatest elongation* for planets? Explain both for planets closer than Earth to the Sun and for planets farther than Earth from the Sun.

4. Under what circumstances do we see a *transit* of a planet across the Sun?

5. What is *apparent solar time*? Why is it different from *mean solar time*? How are *standard time, daylight saving time,* and *universal time* related to mean solar time?

6. Describe the origins of the Julian and Gregorian calendars. Which one do we use today?

7. What do we mean when we say the equinoxes and solstices are points on the celestial sphere? How are these points related to the times of year called the equinoxes and solstices?

8. What are *declination* and *right ascension*? How are these celestial coordinates similar to latitude and longitude on Earth? How are they different?

9. How and why do the Sun's celestial coordinates change over the course of each year?

10. Suppose you are standing at the North Pole. Where is the celestial equator in your sky? Where is the north celestial pole? Describe the daily motion of the sky. Do the same for the sky at the equator and at latitude 40°N.

11. Describe the Sun's path through the local sky on the equinoxes and on the solstices for latitude 40°N. Do the same for the North Pole, South Pole, and equator.

12. What is special about the tropics of Cancer and Capricorn? Describe the Sun's path on the solstices at these latitudes. Do the same for the Arctic and Antarctic Circles.

13. Briefly describe how you can use the Sun or stars to determine your latitude and longitude.

14. What is the global positioning system (GPS)?

TEST YOUR UNDERSTANDING

Does It Make Sense?

Decide whether the statement makes sense (or is clearly true) or does not make sense (or is clearly false). Explain clearly; not all of these have definitive answers, so your explanation is more important than your chosen answer.

(Hint: For statements that involve coordinates—such as altitude, longitude, or declination—check whether the correct coordinates are used for the situation. For example, it does not make sense to describe a location on Earth by an altitude, because altitude only describes positions of objects in the local sky.)

15. Last night I saw Venus shining brightly on the meridian at midnight.

16. The apparent solar time was noon, but the Sun was just setting.

17. My mean solar clock said it was 2:00 p.m., but a friend who lives east of here had a mean solar clock that said it was 2:11 p.m.

18. When the standard time is 3:00 p.m. in Baltimore, it is 3:15 p.m. in Washington, D.C.

19. Last night around 8:00 p.m., I saw Jupiter at an altitude of 45° in the south.

20. The latitude of the stars in Orion's belt is about 5°N.

21. Today the Sun is at an altitude of 10° on the celestial sphere.

22. Los Angeles is west of New York by about 3 hours of right ascension.

23. The summer solstice is east of the vernal equinox by 6 hours of right ascension.

24. Even though my UT clock had stopped, I was able to find my longitude by measuring the altitudes of 14 different stars in my local sky.

Quick Quiz

Choose the best answer to each of the following. Explain your reasoning with one or more complete sentences.

25. The time from one spring equinox to the next is the (a) sidereal day. (b) tropical year. (c) synodic month.

26. Jupiter is brightest when it is (a) at opposition. (b) at conjunction. (c) closest to the Sun in its orbit.

27. Venus is easiest to see in the evening when it is (a) at superior conjunction. (b) at inferior conjunction. (c) at greatest eastern elongation.

28. In the winter, your wristwatch tells (a) apparent solar time. (b) standard time. (c) universal time.

29. A star that is located 30° north of the celestial equator has (a) declination = 30°. (b) right ascension = 30°. (c) latitude = 30°.

30. A star's path through your sky depends on your latitude and the star's (a) declination. (b) right ascension. (c) both declination and right ascension.

31. At latitude 50°N, the celestial equator crosses the meridian at altitude (a) 50° in the south. (b) 50° in the north. (c) 40° in the south.

32. At the North Pole on the summer solstice, the Sun (a) remains stationary in the sky. (b) reaches the zenith at noon. (c) circles the horizon at altitude $23\frac{1}{2}°$.

33. If you know a star's declination, you can determine your latitude if you also (a) measure its altitude when it crosses the meridian. (b) measure its right ascension. (c) know the universal time.

34. If you measure the Sun's position in your local sky, you can determine your longitude if you also (a) measure its altitude when it crosses the meridian. (b) know its right ascension and declination. (c) know the universal time.

PROCESS OF SCIENCE

Examining How Science Works

35. *Transits and the Geocentric Universe.* Ancient people could not observe transits of Mercury or Venus across the Sun, because they lacked instruments for viewing a small dark spot against the Sun. But suppose they could have seen a transit. Would this observation have provided evidence against the Earth-centered universe? If so, explain why. If not, can you think of any related observations that qualify as evidence against the geocentric view? (*Hint:* See Figure 3.24.)

36. *Geometry and Science.* As discussed in Mathematical Insight S1.1, Copernicus found that a Sun-centered model led him to a simple geometric layout for the solar system, a fact that gave him confidence that his model was on the right track. Did the mathematics actually prove that the Sun-centered model was correct, or was it just one step in the longer process of the

Copernican revolution? Use your answer to briefly discuss the role of mathematics in science.

37. *Daylight Saving Time.* Find out why Congress decided to extend the period of daylight saving time by four additional weeks, starting in 2007. Do you think this change was based on science? Defend your opinion.

INVESTIGATE FURTHER

In-Depth Questions to Increase Your Understanding

Short-Answer/Essay Questions

38. *Opposite Rotation.* Suppose Earth rotated in a direction opposite to its orbital direction; that is, suppose it rotated clockwise (as seen from above the North Pole) but orbited counterclockwise. Would the solar day still be longer than the sidereal day? Explain.

39. *No Precession.* Suppose Earth's axis did *not* precess. Would the sidereal year still be different from the tropical year? Explain.

40. *Fundamentals of Your Local Sky.* Answer each of the following for *your* latitude.
    a. Where is the north (or south) celestial pole in your sky?
    b. Describe the location of the meridian in your sky. Specify its shape and at least three distinct points along it (such as the points at which it meets your horizon and its highest point).
    c. Describe the location of the celestial equator in your sky. Specify its shape and at least three distinct points along it (such as the points at which it meets your horizon and crosses your meridian).   d. Does the Sun ever appear at your zenith? If so, when? If not, why not?   e. What range of declinations makes a star circumpolar in your sky? Explain.   f. What is the range of declinations for stars that you can never see in your sky? Explain.

41. *Sydney Sky.* Repeat Problem 40 for the local sky in Sydney, Australia (latitude 34°S).

42. *Local Path of the Sun.* Describe the path of the Sun through your local sky for each of the following days.
    a. The spring and fall equinoxes   b. The summer solstice   c. The winter solstice   d. Today (*Hint:* Estimate the right ascension and declination of the Sun for today's date by using the data in Table S1.1).

43. *Sydney Sun.* Repeat Problem 42 for the local sky in Sydney, Australia (latitude 34°S).

44. *Lost at Sea I.* During a vacation, you decide to take a solo boat trip. While contemplating the universe, you lose track of your location. Fortunately, you have some astronomical tables and instruments, as well as a UT clock. You thereby put together the following description of your situation:
    - It is the spring equinox.
    - The Sun is on your meridian at altitude 75° in the south.
    - The UT clock reads 22:00.
    a. What is your latitude? How do you know?   b. What is your longitude? How do you know?   c. Consult a map. Based on your position, where is the nearest land? Which way should you sail to reach it?

45. *Lost at Sea II.* Repeat Problem 44, based on the following description of your situation:
    - It is the day of the summer solstice.
    - The Sun is on your meridian at altitude $67\frac{1}{2}°$ in the north.
    - The UT clock reads 06:00.

46. *Lost at Sea III.* Repeat Problem 44, based on the following description of your situation:
    - Your local time is midnight.
    - Polaris appears at altitude 67° in the north.
    - The UT clock reads 01:00.

47. *Lost at Sea IV.* Repeat Problem 44, based on the following description of your situation:
    - Your local time is 6 a.m.
    - From the position of the Southern Cross, you estimate that the south celestial pole is at altitude 33° in the south.
    - The UT clock reads 11:00.

48. *The Sun from Mars.* Mars has an axis tilt of 25.2°, only slightly larger than that of Earth. Compared to Earth, is the range of latitudes on Mars for which the Sun can reach the zenith larger or smaller? Is the range of latitudes for which the Sun is circumpolar larger or smaller? Make a sketch of Mars similar to the one for Earth in Figure S1.18.

Quantitative Problems

Be sure to show all calculations clearly and state your final answers in complete sentences.

49. *Solar and Sidereal Days.* Suppose Earth orbited the Sun in 6 months rather than 1 year but had the same rotation period. How much longer would a solar day be than a sidereal day? Explain.

50. *Saturn's Orbital Period.* Saturn's synodic period is 378.1 days. What is its actual orbital period?

51. *Mercury's Orbital Period.* Mercury's synodic period is 115.9 days. What is its actual orbital period?

52. *New Asteroid.* You discover an asteroid with a synodic period of 429 days. What is its actual orbital period?

53. *Using the Analemma I.* It's February 15 and your sundial tells you the apparent solar time is 18 minutes until noon. What is the mean solar time?

54. *Using the Analemma II.* It's July 1 and your sundial tells you that the apparent solar time is 3:30 p.m. What is the mean solar time?

55. *Find the Sidereal Time.* It is 4 p.m. on the spring equinox. What is the local sidereal time?

56. *Where's Vega?* The local sidereal time is 19:30. When will Vega cross your meridian?

57. *Find Right Ascension.* You observe a star that has an hour angle of 13 hours (13^h) when the local sidereal time is 8:15. What is the star's right ascension?

58. *Where's Orion?* The Orion Nebula has declination of about −5.5° and right ascension of 5^h25^m. If you are at latitude 40°N and the local sidereal time is 7:00, approximately where does the Orion Nebula appear in your sky?

59. *Meridian Crossings of the Moon and Phobos.* Estimate the time between meridian crossings of the Moon for a person standing on Earth. Repeat your calculation for meridian crossings of the Martian moon Phobos. Use the Appendices in the back of the book if necessary.

60. *Mercury's Rotation Period.* Mercury's sidereal day is approximately $\frac{2}{3}$ of its orbital period, or about 58.6 days. Estimate the length of Mercury's solar day. Compare it to Mercury's orbital period of about 88 days.

Discussion Questions

61. *Northern Chauvinism.* Why is the solstice in June called the *summer solstice,* when it marks winter for places like Australia, New Zealand, and South Africa? Why is the writing on maps and globes usually oriented so that the Northern Hemisphere is at the top, even though there is no up or down in space? Discuss.

62. *Celestial Navigation.* Briefly discuss how you think the benefits and problems of celestial navigation might have affected ancient sailors. For example, how did they benefit from using the north celestial pole to tell directions, and what problems did they

experience because of the difficulty in determining longitude? Can you explain why ancient sailors generally hugged coastlines as much as possible on their voyages? What dangers did this type of sailing pose? Why did the Polynesians become the best navigators of their time?

Web Projects

63. *Sundials.* Although they are no longer necessary for timekeeping, sundials remain popular for their cultural and artistic value. Search the Web for pictures and information about sundials around the world. Write a short report about three sundials that you find particularly interesting.

64. *The Analemma.* Use the Web to learn more about the analemma and its uses. Write a short report on your findings.

65. *Calendar History.* Investigate the history of the Julian or Gregorian calendar in greater detail. Write a short summary of an interesting aspect of the history you learn from your Web research. (For example, why did Julius Caesar allow one year to have 445 days? How did our months end up with 28, 30, or 31 days?)

66. *Global Positioning System.* Learn more about the global positioning system and its uses. Write a short report summarizing how you think the growing availability of GPS will affect our lives over the next 10 years.

VISUAL SKILLS CHECK

Use the following questions to check your understanding of some of the many types of visual information used in astronomy. Answers are provided in Appendix J. For additional practice, try the Chapter S1 Visual Quiz at www.masteringastronomy.com.

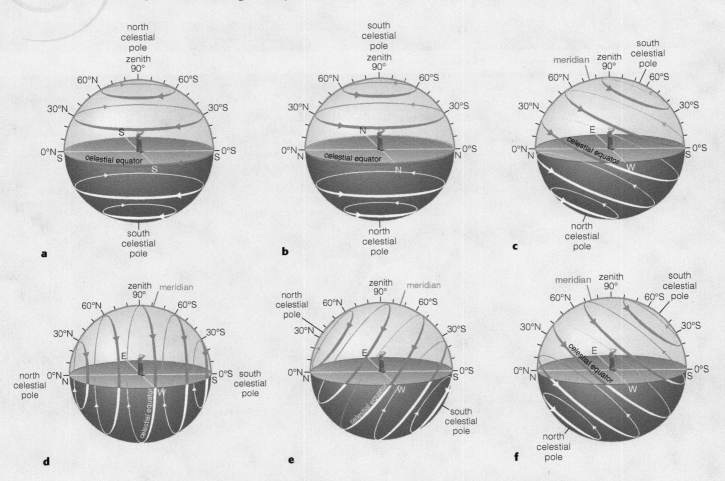

The six diagrams above represent the sky at six different latitudes. Answer the following questions about them.

1. Which diagram represents the paths of stars at the North Pole?
2. Which diagram represents the paths of stars at the South Pole?
3. Which diagrams represent Southern Hemisphere skies?
4. What latitude is represented in diagram c?
5. Which diagram(s) represent(s) a latitude at which the Sun sometimes passes directly overhead?
6. Which diagram(s) represent(s) a latitude at which the Sun sometimes remains below the horizon during a full 24-hour period?
7. Each diagram shows five star circles. Look at the first circle to the north of the celestial equator on each diagram. Can you characterize the *declination* of stars on this circle? If so, what is it? Can you characterize the *right ascension* of stars on this circle? If so, what is it?

Our perspective on the universe has changed dramatically throughout human history. This timeline summarizes some of the key discoveries that have shaped our modern perspective.

Stonehenge

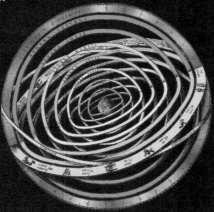

Earth-centered model of the universe

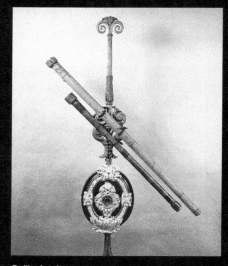

Galileo's telescope

| < 2500 B.C. | 400 B.C. –170 A.D. | 1543–1648 A.D. |

(1) Ancient civilizations recognized patterns in the motion of the Sun, Moon, planets, and stars through our sky. They also noticed connections between what they saw in the sky and our lives on Earth, such as the cycles of seasons and of tides [Section 3.1].

(2) The ancient Greeks tried to explain observed motions of the Sun, Moon, and planets using a model with Earth at the center, surrounded by spheres in the heavens. The model explained many phenomena well, but could explain the apparent retrograde motion of the planets only with the addition of many complex features—and even then, its predictions were not especially accurate [Section 3.2].

(3) Copernicus suggested that Earth is a planet orbiting the Sun. The Sun-centered model explained apparent retrograde motion simply, though it made accurate predictions only after Kepler discovered his three laws of planetary motion. Galileo's telescopic observations confirmed the Sun-centered model, and revealed that the universe contains far more stars than had been previously imagined [Section 3.3].

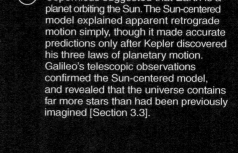

Earth's rotation around its axis leads to the daily east-to-west motions of objects in the sky.

The tilt of Earth's rotation axis leads to seasons as Earth orbits the Sun.

Planets are much smaller than the Sun. At a scale of 1-to-10 billion, the Sun is the size of a grapefruit, Earth is the size of a ball point of a pen, and the distance between them is about 15 meters.

Yerkes Observatory

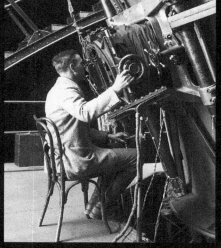

Edwin Hubble at the Mt. Wilson telescope

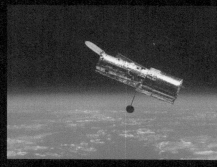

Hubble Space Telescope

1838–1920 A.D.   1924–1929 A.D.   1990 A.D.–present

(4) Larger telescopes and photography made it possible to measure the parallax of stars, offering direct proof that Earth really does orbit the Sun and showing that even the nearest stars are light-years away. We learned that our Sun is a fairly ordinary star in the Milky Way [Section 2.4, 15.1].

(5) Edwin Hubble measured the distances of galaxies, showing that they lay far beyond the bounds of the Milky Way and proving that the universe is far larger than our own galaxy. He also discovered that more distant galaxies are moving away from us faster, telling us that the entire universe is expanding and suggesting that it began in an event we call the Big Bang [Section 1.3, 20.2].

(6) Improved measurements of galactic distances and the rate of expansion have shown that the universe is about 14 billion years old. These measurements have also revealed still-unexplained surprises, including evidence for the existence of mysterious "dark matter" and "dark energy" [Section 1.3, 22.1].

Distances between stars are enormous. At a scale of 1-to-10 billion, you can hold the Sun in your hand, but the nearest stars are thousands of kilometers away.

Our solar system is located about 28,000 light-years from the center of the Milky Way Galaxy.

The Milky Way Galaxy contains over 100 billion stars.

The observable universe contains over 100 billion galaxies.

I STAR CHARTS

How to use the star charts:

Check the times and dates under each chart to find the best one for you. Take it outdoors within an hour or so of the time listed for your date. Bring a dim flashlight to help you read it.

On each chart, the round outside edge represents the horizon all around you. Compass directions around the horizon are marked in yellow. Turn the chart around so that the edge marked with the direction you're facing (for example, north, southeast) is down. The stars above this horizon now match the stars you are facing. Ignore the rest until you turn to look in a different direction.

The center of the chart represents the sky overhead, so a star plotted on the chart halfway from the edge to the center can be found in the sky halfway from the horizon to straight up.

The charts are drawn for 40°N latitude (for example, Denver, New York, Madrid). If you live far south of there, stars in the southern part of your sky will appear higher than on the chart and stars in the north will be lower. If you live far north of there, the reverse is true.

Jan.–March
© Sky Publishing Corp.

© 1999 *Sky & Telescope*

Use this chart January, February, and March.

Early January—1 a.m.
Late January—Midnight

Early February—11 p.m.
Late February—10 p.m.

Early March—9 p.m.
Late March—Dusk

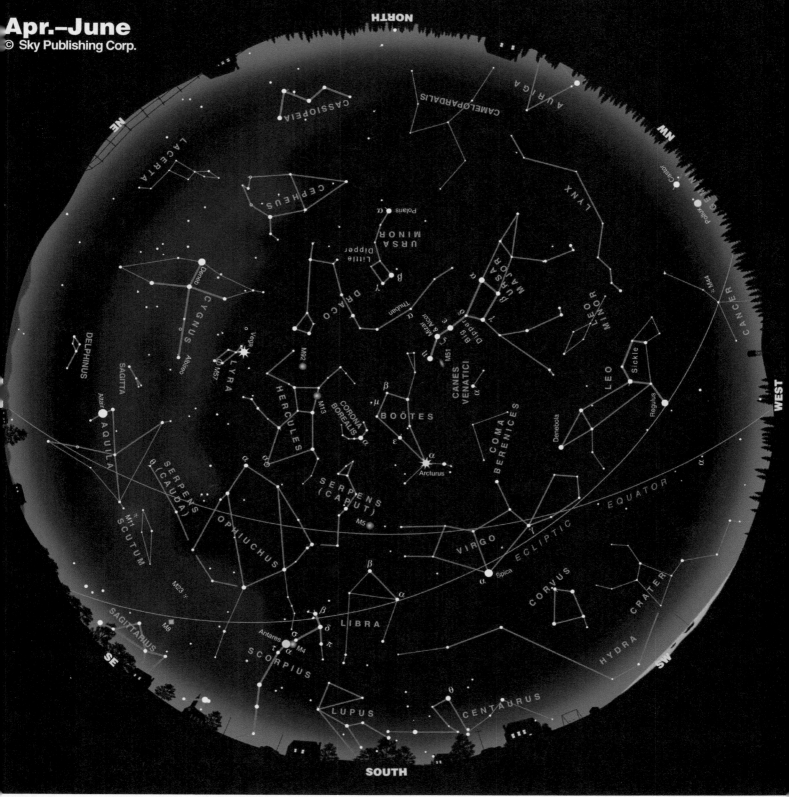

Apr.–June

Use this chart April, May, and June.

Early April—3 a.m.*   Early May—1 a.m.*   Early June—11 p.m.*
Late April—2 a.m.*   Late May—Midnight*   Late June—Dusk

*Daylight Saving Time

July–Sept.
© Sky Publishing Corp.

© 1999 *Sky & Telescope*

Use this chart July, August, and September.

Early July—1 a.m.
Late July—Midnight*

Early August—11 p.m.*
Late August—10 p.m.*

Early September—9 p.m.*
Late September—Dusk

*Daylight Saving Time

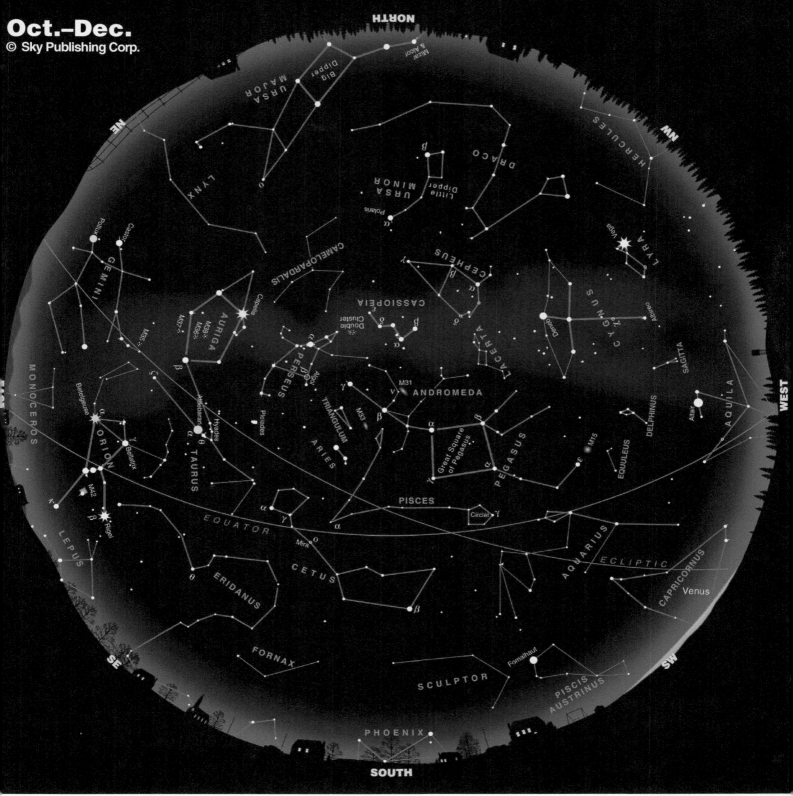

Oct.–Dec.
© Sky Publishing Corp.

© 1999 *Sky & Telescope*

Use this chart October, November, and December.

Early October—1 a.m.*   Early November—10 p.m.   Early December—8 p.m.
Late October—Midnight*   Late November—9 p.m.   Late December—7 p.m.

*Daylight Saving Time

J ANSWERS TO VISUAL SKILLS CHECK QUESTIONS

Chapter 1
1. b
2. c
3. c
4. No; the nearest stars would not fit on Earth on this scale.

Chapter 2
1. B
2. D
3. A
4. C
5. d
6. d
7. c
8. c

Chapter 3
1. d
2. b
3. d
4. a
5. a
6. a
7. a

Chapter S1
1. a
2. b
3. b, c, f
4. 66.5°S (the Antarctic Circle)
5. d
6. a, b, c
7. Declination is +30°; right ascension cannot be characterized without further information.

Chapter 4
1. b
2. d
3. a
4. d
5. c

Chapter 5
1. 5
2. 1
3. b
4. b
5. c

Chapter 6
1. b
2. a, c, e
3. all
4. a
5. a

Chapter 7
1. From A to H, the planets are Mercury, Mars, Venus, Earth, Neptune, Uranus, Saturn, and Jupiter.
2. The pairs are Mercury and Mars, Venus and Earth, Neptune and Uranus, Saturn and Jupiter.
3. d
4. a. The exponential plot shows information on low-mass planets that can't be seen on the linear plot.
   b. The linear plot
   c. The exponential plot

Chapter 8
1. a
2. e
3. c

Chapter 9
1. a
2. c
3. b
4. b, c, a

Chapter 10
1. d
2. b
3. d
4. c
5. b

Chapter 11
1. c
2. c
3. b
4. b

Chapter 12
1. about 5 km, though its unusual shape could lead to answers between 4 and 8 km
2. b
3. a
4. c
5. b

Chapter 13
1. about 4 days
2. about 50 meters/sec
3. a. 2 b. 4 c. 3 d. 1
4. a. 4 b. 2 c. 1 d. 3
5. b

Chapter 14
1. d
2. Sunspots appear over a range of 40–50°N latitude to 40–50°S latitude.
3. Sunspots get closer to the equator during a sunspot cycle.

Chapter 15
1. b
2. d
3. c
4. luminosity: about $10,000L_{Sun}$; lifetime: slightly longer than 10 million years
5. luminosity: about $30L_{Sun}$; lifetime: approximately 1 billion years

Chapter 16
1. 200–300 light-years
2. About 1000 light-years
3. Cool gas is mostly in the centers of the streams.
4. The cold gas heats up when it enters the central cloud.

Chapter 17

1. approximately $10L_{Sun}$
2. approximately 3500 K
3. approximately $10^4 L_{Sun}$
4. approximately $10^{-4} L_{Sun}$

Chapter 18

1. b
2. d
3. b
4. c
5. d

Chapter 19

1. brightest: white; lowest levels of brightness: black/dark blue
2. white
3. Regions with strong radio emission are dark in the visible-light image.
4. Regions with strong radio emission are brighter in the infrared image than they are in the visible-light image.
5. c
6. yes

Chapter 20

1. Cepheids
2. parallax
3. approximately 100–100,000 light-years
4. from about 30 million light-years to more than 10 billion light-years
5. Cepheids
6. distant standards and Hubble's law

Chapter 21

1. white
2. purple
3. approximately 400,000 light-years
4. approximately 20,000 light-years

Chapter 22

1. accelerating
2. accelerating
3. coasting
4. decelerating

Chapter 23

1. d
2. d
3. d
4. a

Chapter 24

1. g, f, b, e, d, c, a
2. b, a, c, d
3. a, c, d
4. d
5. c
6. c